Genetic INNOVATION

1985 TO 1995

Published by The Reader's Digest Association, Inc.
London • New York • Sydney • Montreal

Newton
Names
Dates
Extras
Undo
Find
Assist
MessagePad
SONY
PlayStation
START
ANALOG

Contents

Introduction

Some historians would argue that the 21st century really got under way not with the year 2000 but rather in November 1989, with the dismantling of the Berlin Wall. In short order the Communist bloc collapsed, undermined by the reforming zeal of Mikhail Gorbachev in the USSR and the Polish revolt led by Lech Walesa. A victorious USA took up the reins of the new world order, and has yet to put them down again. Western Europe overcame its worries about the prospect of a reunited Germany and opening up to the East, embarking instead on a new phase of consolidation, doing away with borders and extending the single market. Asia profited from the optimistic outlook; the four 'tiger' economies – South Korea, Hong Kong, Singapore and Taiwan – surged ahead. China began to flirt with capitalism and India displayed a burgeoning interest in high technology.

The globalisation of the world economy went hand in hand with the development of the Internet, virtual imagery and the information

Listening to the universe
The Arecibo radio telescope in Puerto Rico was built in the early 1960s. The huge collecting disc is made up of almost 39,000 aluminium panels and measures 305m (1,000ft) across. The telescope is operated by Cornell University, where Carl Sagan was appointed professor of astronomy and space science in 1971.

society, favouring a consumerist model of growth based on continual innovation. At the same time an awareness of the long-term need for some more sustainable development path, founded on ethical principles, was also making itself felt. Discoveries in the field of DNA set in motion a true scientific revolution, bringing hope of genetic treatments for a number of diseases, but also fears of unforeseen consequences if researchers failed to respect human sensibilities.

The first Gulf War broke out in 1990, confirming both the strategic importance of the Middle East and the dominant influence of the USA, which had taken up the role of the world's policeman. The following year Europe, which had hoped to have left the shadow of war behind for ever, saw a fracturing Yugoslavia descend into violence and 'ethnic cleansing', forcing the continent to confront once more its old nationalist demons. Big ideas of universal peace and harmony ran up against the rise of communal allegiances and religious extremism, an old foe reborn. Seeking distraction from such developments, people found solace in the world of computers and video games.

The editors

▼ The renowned British geneticist Alec Jeffreys developed DNA profiling techniques that made it possible to identify sequences serving as individual genetic signatures

► The hero of a world-famous Nintendo series, Super Mario brought new life to video games, which had first been developed in the late 1950s

► In 1987 astrophysicists discovered that stars are created from huge stellar clouds of gas and dust like this one

The late 1980s saw dramatic progress in the field of genetics. With the discovery of genetic profiling, every individual human being could now be identified by a unique code, providing forensic science with a valuable new tool. The sequencing of the human

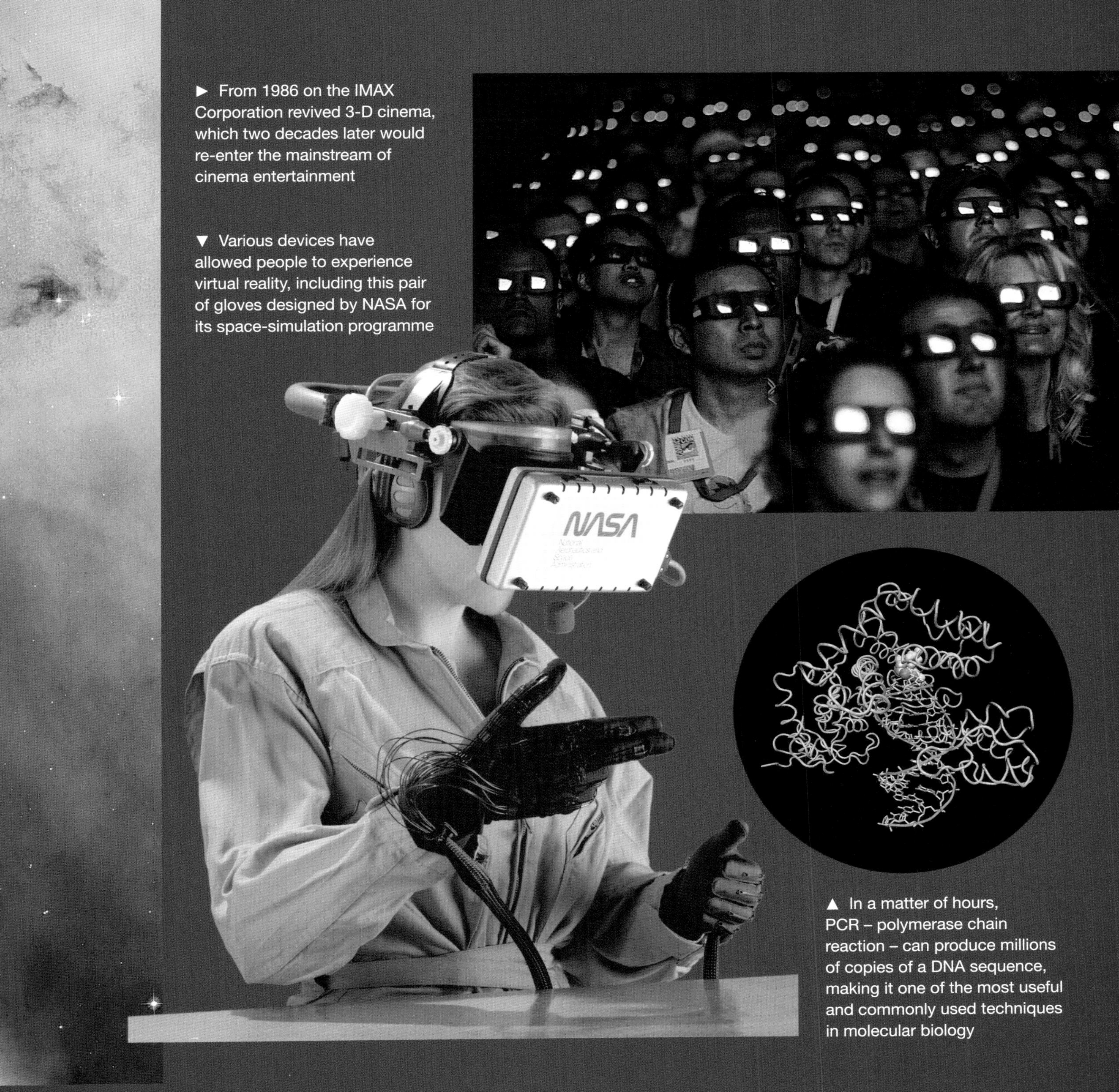

► From 1986 on the IMAX Corporation revived 3-D cinema, which two decades later would re-enter the mainstream of cinema entertainment

▼ Various devices have allowed people to experience virtual reality, including this pair of gloves designed by NASA for its space-simulation programme

▲ In a matter of hours, PCR – polymerase chain reaction – can produce millions of copies of a DNA sequence, making it one of the most useful and commonly used techniques in molecular biology

genome made it possible to single out the genes implicated in conditions such as myopathy (diseases of the muscles) and immune system deficiencies and in some cases to correct them, opening up a whole new world of therapeutic possibilities. Yet as

▲► The Internet had its roots in the technological race between the USA and USSR in the late 1950s, but the global network took off in its present form from 1989; today its presence can be felt in every aspect of life

animal experiments involving genetic engineering showed, it was a small step from therapy to experimentation, and committees set up to consider the ethical implications of genetic manipulation were the only barriers preventing scientists from taking that step.

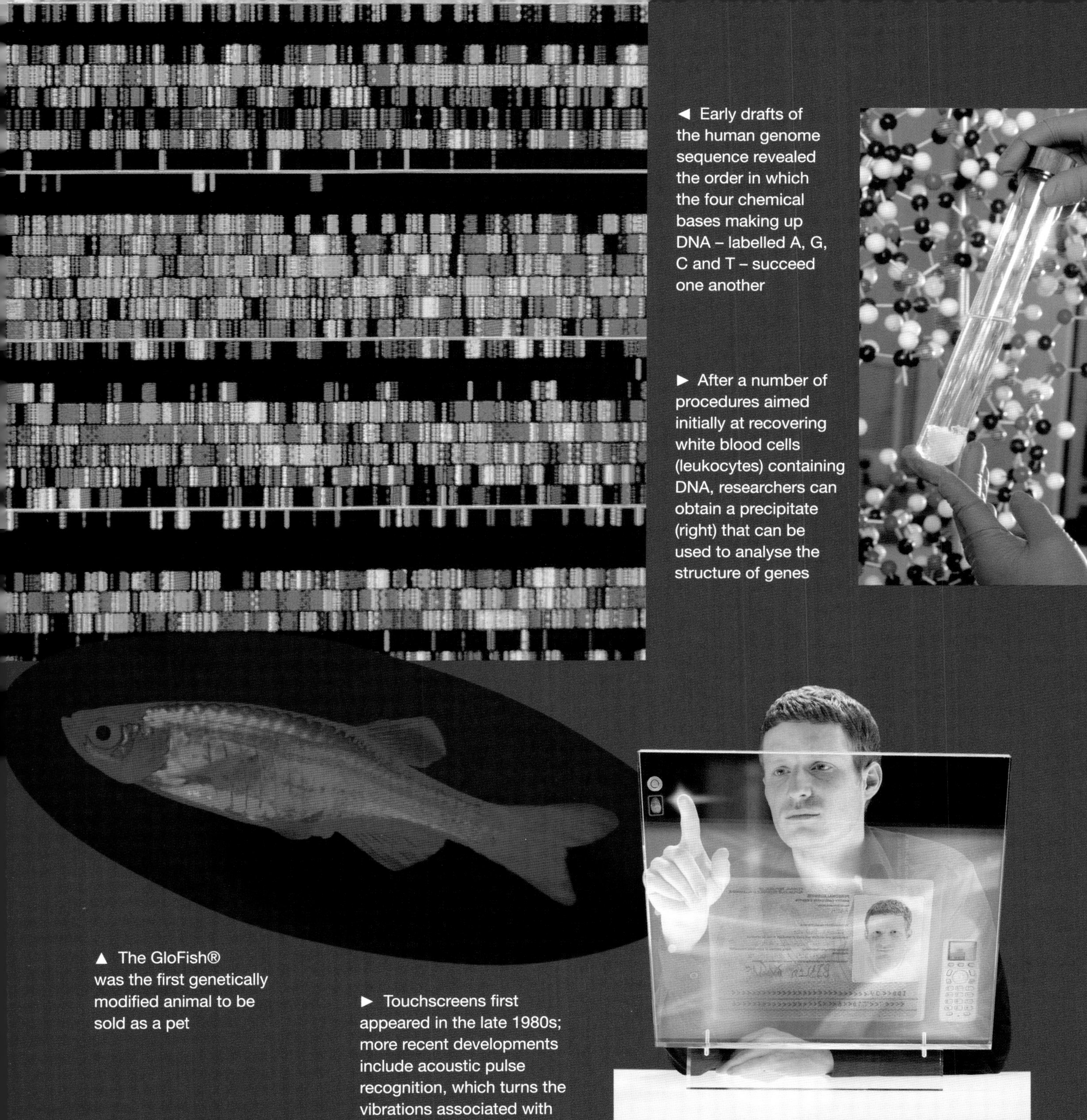

◄ Early drafts of the human genome sequence revealed the order in which the four chemical bases making up DNA – labelled A, G, C and T – succeed one another

► After a number of procedures aimed initially at recovering white blood cells (leukocytes) containing DNA, researchers can obtain a precipitate (right) that can be used to analyse the structure of genes

▲ The GloFish® was the first genetically modified animal to be sold as a pet

► Touchscreens first appeared in the late 1980s; more recent developments include acoustic pulse recognition, which turns the vibrations associated with touch into electronic signals

It was a time for thought and reflection – the 'new improved human' posited by the advance of science had yet to be born. Meanwhile, the onward march of new technology continued, introducing accessories such as personal organisers and digital

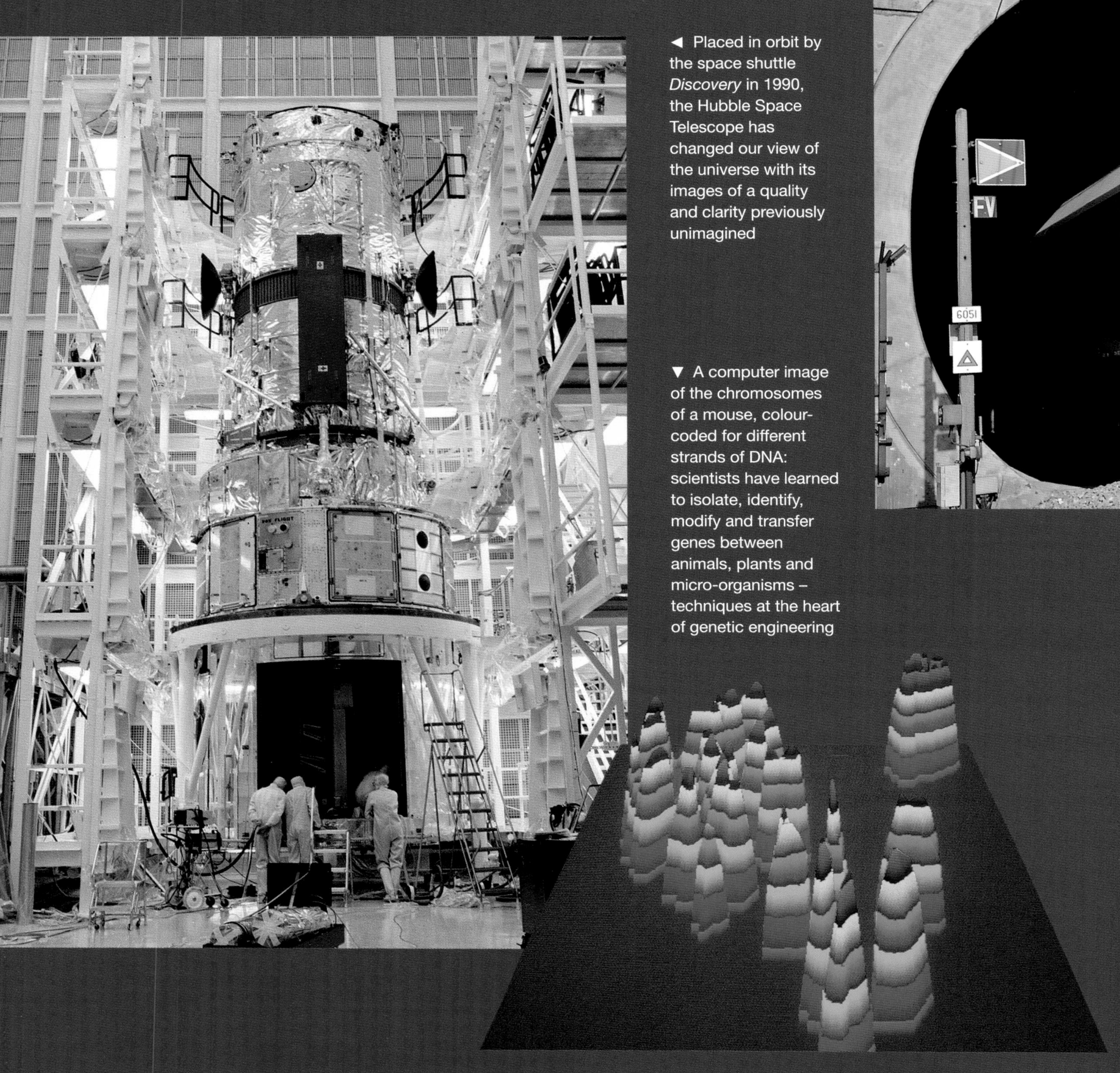

◄ Placed in orbit by the space shuttle *Discovery* in 1990, the Hubble Space Telescope has changed our view of the universe with its images of a quality and clarity previously unimagined

▼ A computer image of the chromosomes of a mouse, colour-coded for different strands of DNA: scientists have learned to isolate, identify, modify and transfer genes between animals, plants and micro-organisms – techniques at the heart of genetic engineering

cameras and making it harder than ever to separate people from their computers, now on the verge of becoming an indispensable companion at home as well as in the office. Software took on increasingly complex tasks, from accountancy to desktop

◄ Opened in 1994, the Channel Tunnel linked Britain physically to Continental Europe for the first time in at least 200,000 years

▲ Around 65 million years ago, 80 per cent of species on Earth, including the dinosaurs, were wiped out; in the 1980s scientists traced the cause to the cataclysmic impact of a giant meteorite striking the planet

▼ The Kinemax in the Futuroscope park at Poitiers in France is part of a new wave of museums and theme parks using interactive displays to popularise science and technology

publishing and industrial design. And the time was coming when computers would provide instant access to information through the Internet, which would profoundly affect everyone's lives. Frontiers were disappearing as virtual reality found a way into daily

► Digital cameras (right and below right) transform images into digital data, doing away with the need for film; initially targeted at the mass market, they have since won over professional photographers

◄ Nanoscience and nanotechnology work with objects as small as 1 nanometre (a millionth of a millimetre) in extent, like these tiny carbon molecules known as fullerenes

life. Video games benefited from advances in computer graphics, while film-makers began to master digital imaging. Cinema also took viewers into the heart of the action via large-screen 3-D films shown in theme parks. A new branch of science emerged in

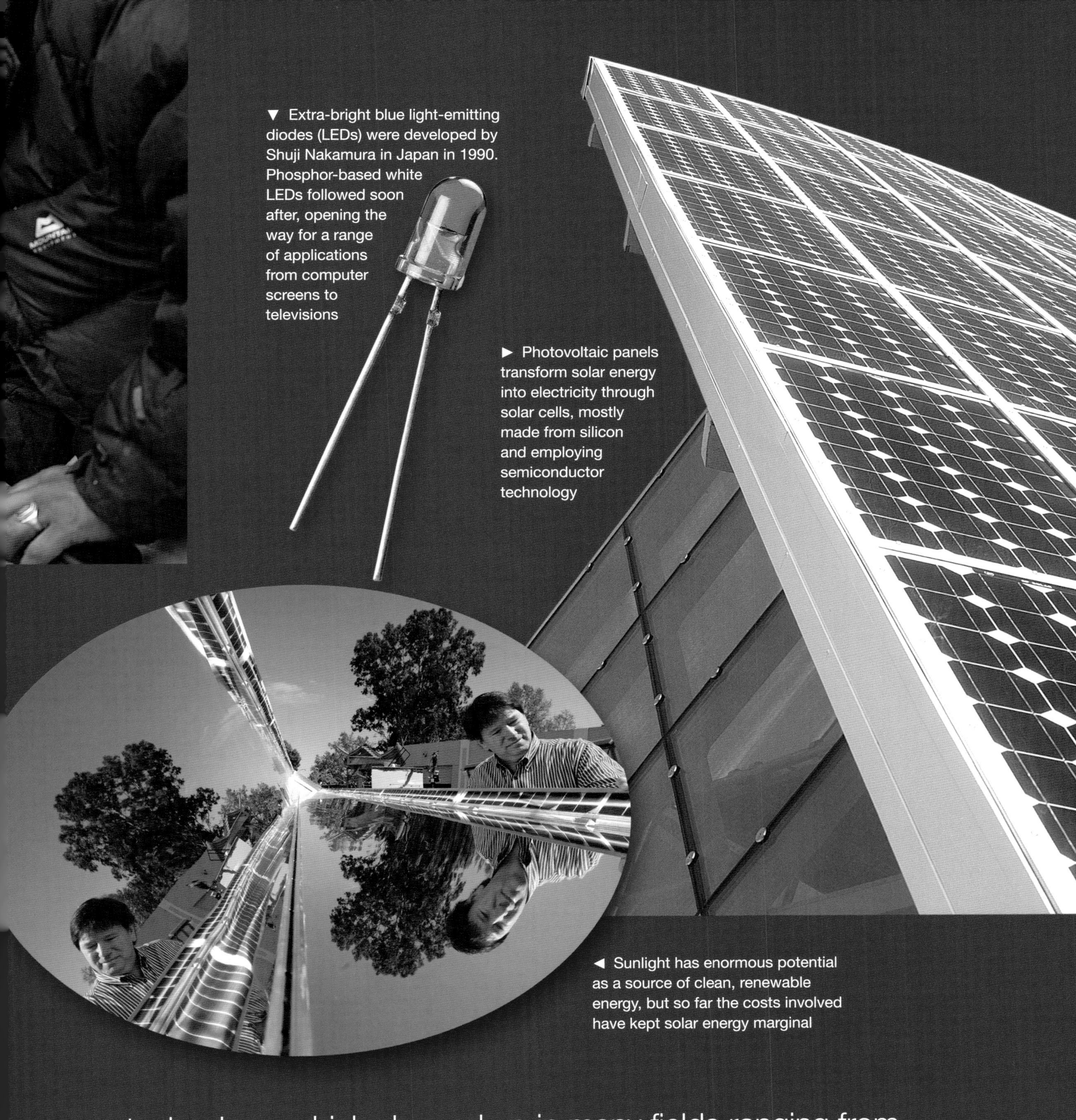

▼ Extra-bright blue light-emitting diodes (LEDs) were developed by Shuji Nakamura in Japan in 1990. Phosphor-based white LEDs followed soon after, opening the way for a range of applications from computer screens to televisions

► Photovoltaic panels transform solar energy into electricity through solar cells, mostly made from silicon and employing semiconductor technology

◄ Sunlight has enormous potential as a source of clean, renewable energy, but so far the costs involved have kept solar energy marginal

nanotechnology, which showed up in many fields ranging from electronics to metallurgy and medicine to food. Growing concerns over the environment encouraged innovations like biodegradable plastics, while solar energy, with its photovoltaic panels and

▲ Superconducting electromagnets are the most important application of superconductivity to date, put to use in particle accelerators like the Large Hadron Collider (LHC) near Geneva – this image from the LHC shows the Compact Muon Solenoid particle detector

▲ Smart materials first made their mark in the world of sport, whether in the form of parabolic skis, ultralight racing cycles, anti-drag swimwear or racing cars employing composite materials and radial tyres

parabolic reflectors, came to be seen as a promising alternative energy source. Astronomers extended their exploration of the heavens to include the hunt for exoplanets – planets outside our Solar System – with conditions similar to those on Earth. To help

► Video offered new opportunities for artists; this 1989 assemblage was by Korean-born artist Nam June Paik

▼ A quantum computer of 2004, a decade after US mathematician Peter Shor showed that quantum computation could be used to devise a calculating machine faster than the most powerful conventional computer possible

◄ Launched in 1995, the DVD was intended as the successor to the CD, sharing the same format but with a vastly enlarged data storage capacity

them they had new tools, such as the Hubble Space Telescope, which over time provided images of the formation of stars and improved our understanding of how the universe works. Back on Earth, life continued to speed up. High-speed ocean-going craft

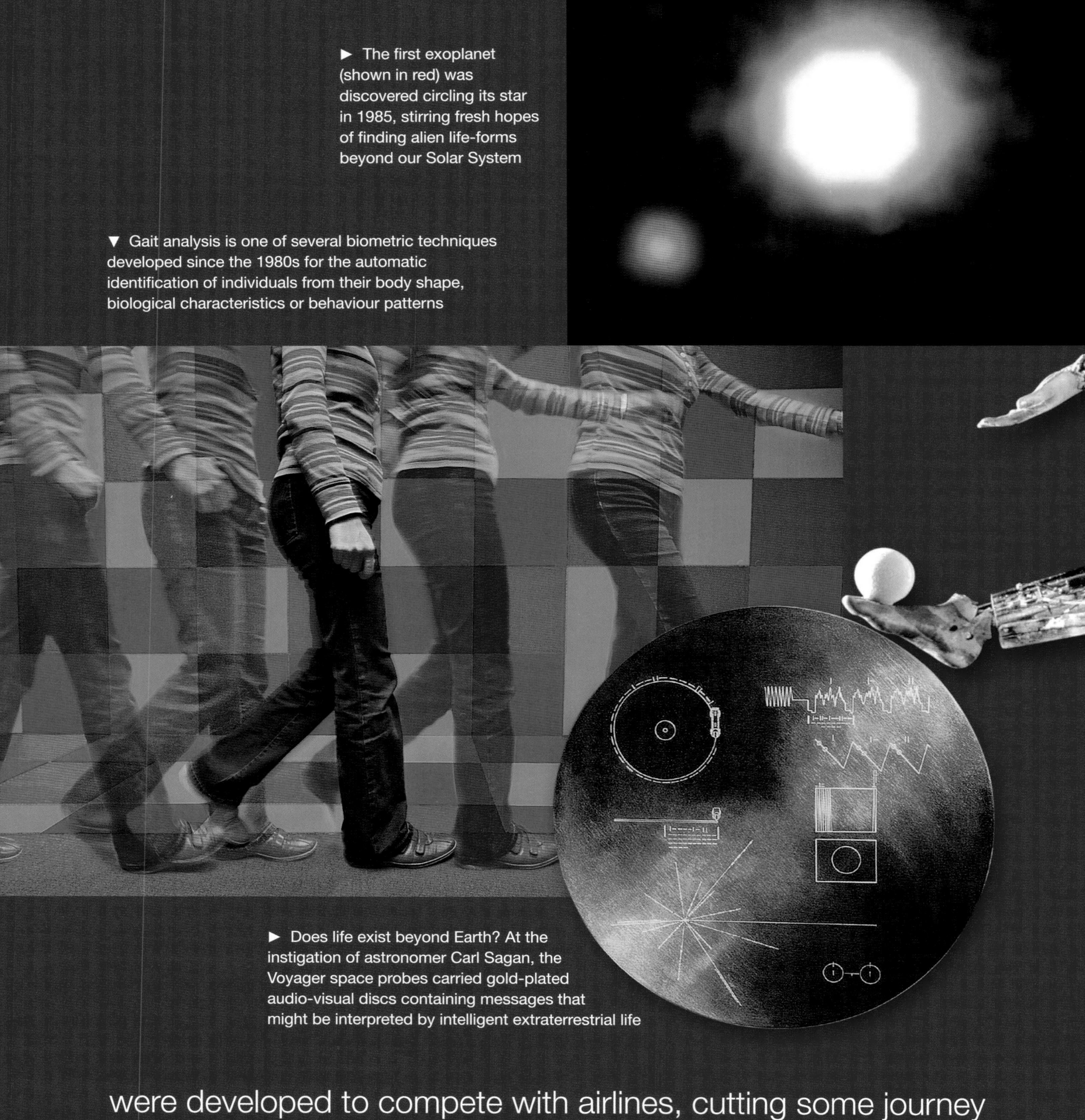

► The first exoplanet (shown in red) was discovered circling its star in 1985, stirring fresh hopes of finding alien life-forms beyond our Solar System

▼ Gait analysis is one of several biometric techniques developed since the 1980s for the automatic identification of individuals from their body shape, biological characteristics or behaviour patterns

► Does life exist beyond Earth? At the instigation of astronomer Carl Sagan, the Voyager space probes carried gold-plated audio-visual discs containing messages that might be interpreted by intelligent extraterrestrial life

were developed to compete with airlines, cutting some journey times in half, while the construction of the Channel Tunnel brought the UK and Continental Europe closer together. In the global village that the increasingly digitised planet was becoming, emerging

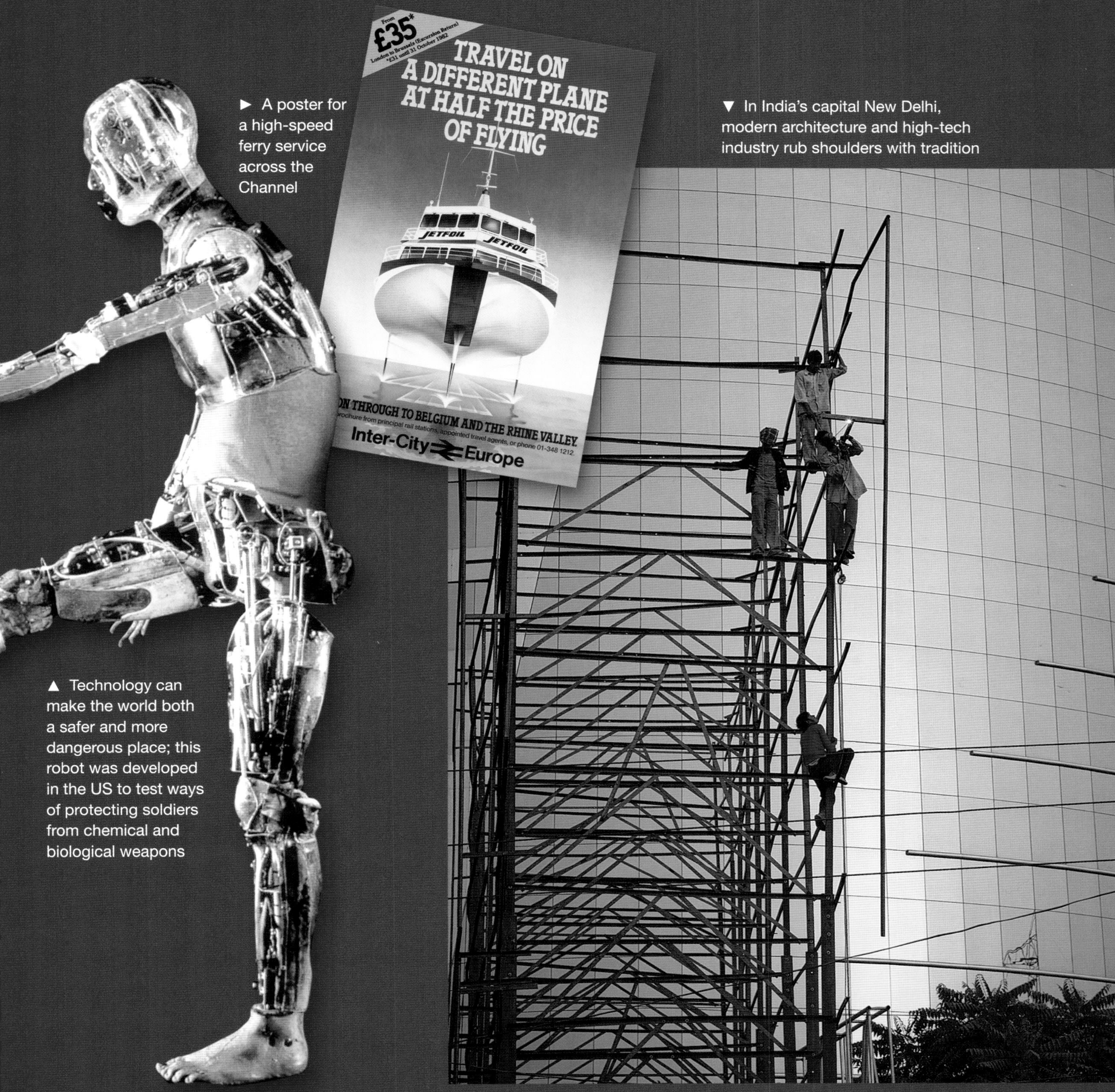

► A poster for a high-speed ferry service across the Channel

▼ In India's capital New Delhi, modern architecture and high-tech industry rub shoulders with tradition

▲ Technology can make the world both a safer and more dangerous place; this robot was developed in the US to test ways of protecting soldiers from chemical and biological weapons

nations played an important part, epitomised by India's capital, New Delhi, which became a centre for software, video games and solar panels. The bipolar Cold War world was giving way to a multi-polar globe whose watchword was interconnection.

THE STORY OF INVENTIONS

In the 1980s the human race acquired the knowledge needed to realise one of its wildest dreams: that of creating living beings. Thanks to advances in genetics, it became possible not just to decipher DNA but also to experiment with it, with the aim of improving our crops and curing diseases. Over the horizon lay the tantalising possibility of improving human faculties. As experts considered the ethical implications, increasing numbers of ordinary mortals satisfied their imaginative impulses by manipulating creatures – many of them monstrous – invented for the virtual world of video games.

GENETIC PROFILING – 1985

The unique fingerprint of DNA

In 1985 the British geneticist Alec Jeffreys developed a technique that would revolutionise crime detection. He isolated fragments of DNA that could be read as a unique fingerprint or signature of the individual involved, allowing people to be identified with almost complete certainty.

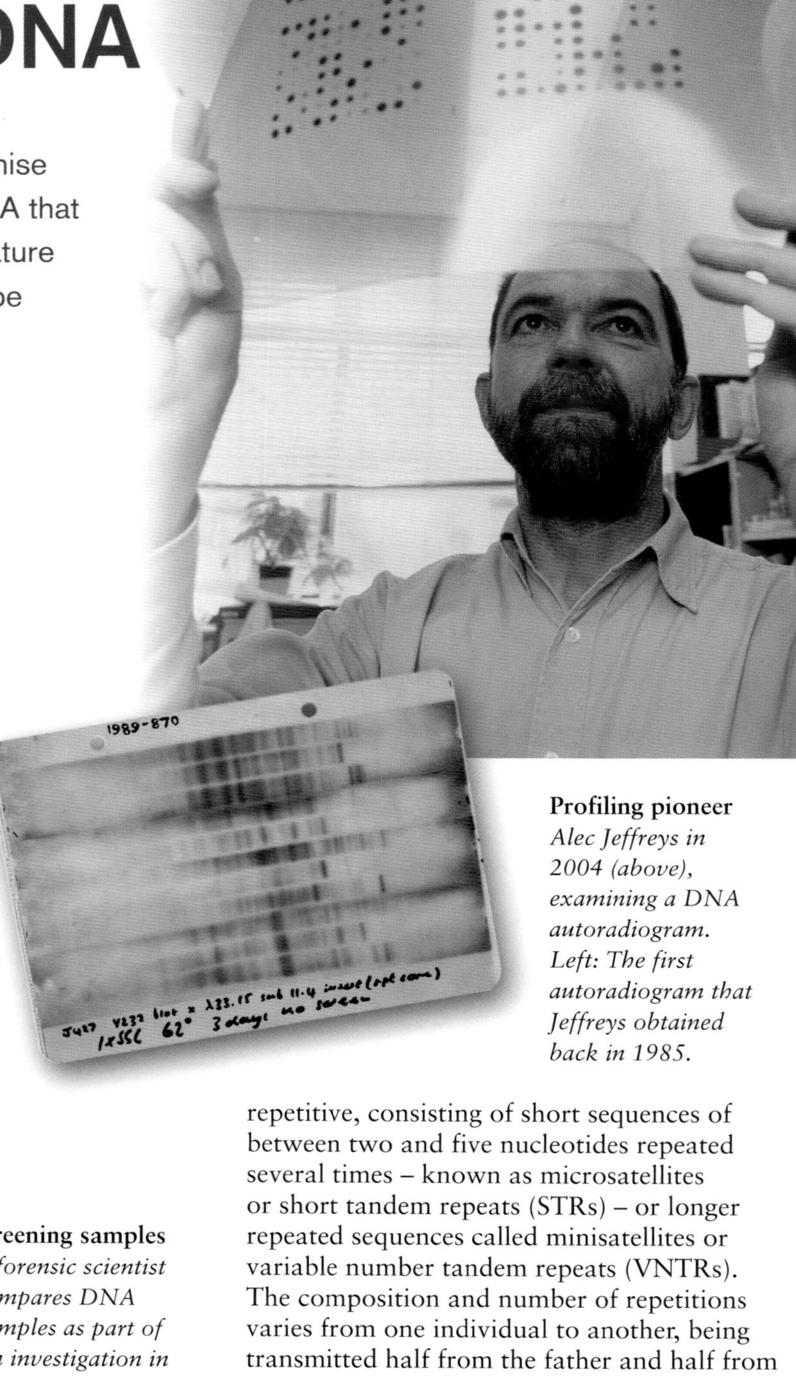

Profiling pioneer
Alec Jeffreys in 2004 (above), examining a DNA autoradiogram. Left: The first autoradiogram that Jeffreys obtained back in 1985.

Professor Jeffreys had been working on DNA at the University of Leicester since 1977, noting the variations in samples taken from different individuals. Between 1978 and 1981 he identified, in some highly variable sections of DNA, a sequence of bases which were always the same. The sequence could be detected because it linked to a complementary 'hook' specific to the individual concerned. It followed that these 'minisatellites', as the sequences are called, could be used as a means of identification. The principle behind genetic fingerprinting was thus established.

A mine of information

DNA is formed of different sequences of four nucleotide bases, adenine, thymine, guanine and cytosine (A, T, G and C). Genes are sections of DNA that may either be coding (for ethnic origin, eye colour or some other trait, for example) or noncoding. The latter are repetitive, consisting of short sequences of between two and five nucleotides repeated several times – known as microsatellites or short tandem repeats (STRs) – or longer repeated sequences called minisatellites or variable number tandem repeats (VNTRs). The composition and number of repetitions varies from one individual to another, being transmitted half from the father and half from the mother. Their exact position or locus (gene segment) on the DNA, established over a number of years, enables scientists to compare sequences, known as polymorphisms.

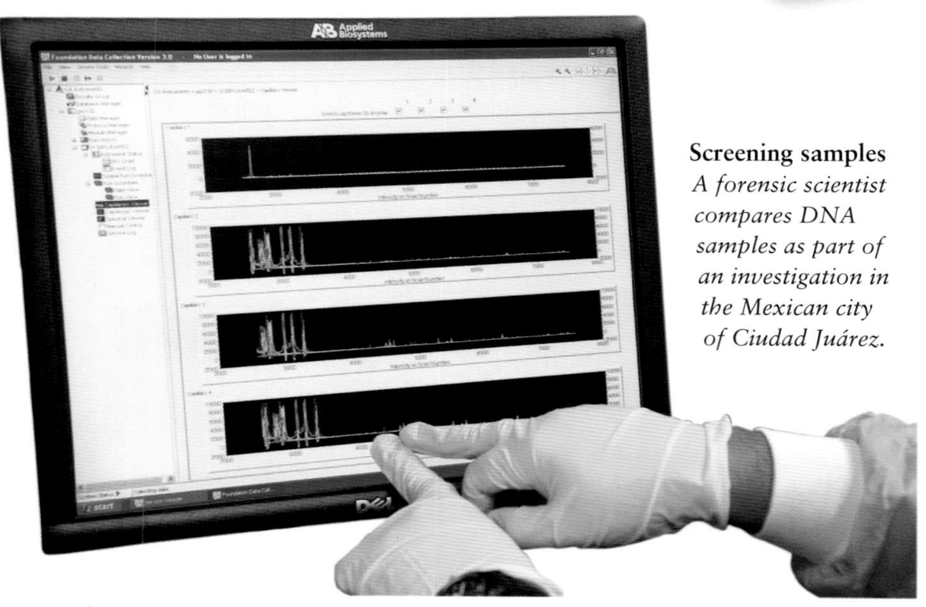

Screening samples
A forensic scientist compares DNA samples as part of an investigation in the Mexican city of Ciudad Juárez.

Genetic profiling in practice

DNA is extracted from the nuclei of cells obtained from a person's mouth or from bodily fluids, organic remains or hairs. Today, the variable sequences are multiplied

DNA DATABASES AND THE LAW

Most European countries keep genetic records, many of which start with individuals supplying samples of cheek cells or saliva (right). In Britain, where the law allows police to take DNA from suspects at the time of arrest, the National DNA Database has profiles of more than 4.5 million people, one in five of whom do not have a criminal record of any kind. In contrast, Germany only stores DNA details of repeat offenders. The criteria in France, initially limited to sex criminals and those guilty of crimes against minors, have been extended but the database still only covers some 80,000 people. The European Court of Human Rights has declared that Britain's policy of holding DNA details of non-convicted people 'could not be regarded as necessary in a democratic society'.

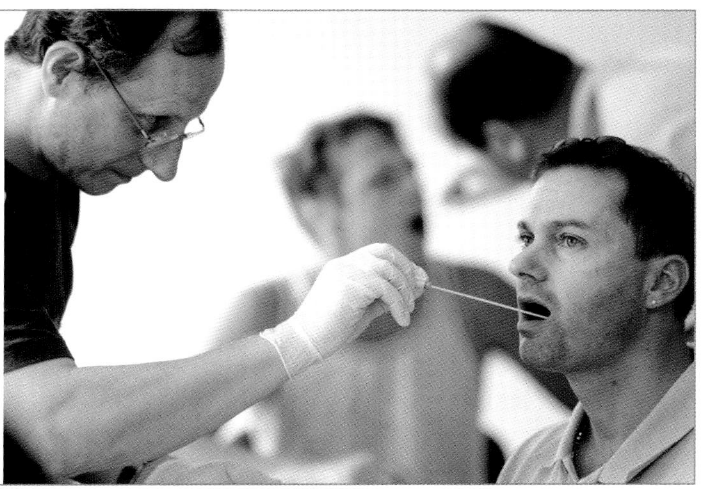

by polymerase chain reaction (PCR) techniques in order to obtain many copies of each locus. The different fragments have an electric surface charge that allows them to be separated and automatically sequenced by electrophoresis. In the early days Jeffreys used restriction enzymes for this separation process: the enzymes cut the DNA molecule in different places, making it possible to isolate fragments containing minisatellites. These were then separated, transferred to a nylon membrane and irradiated, then revealed by radiography, eventually with the aid of an autoradiogram. This slow, delicate method is little used today.

Tutankhamun's genetic inheritance
In 2010 tests of Tutankhamun's DNA confirmed that he was the son of his predecessor, Pharaoh Akhenaten, but showed that his mother was not Nefertiti, the principal queen, but a sister-wife of Akhenaten.

Forensic safeguards

The only people with exactly the same DNA as another individual are identical twins, but each polymorphism can be found with some frequency within a given population, so a match of single polymorphism is not sufficiently specified to identify a subject. Forensic scientists use several different loci for identification purposes – often a standard grouping of 13 polymorphisms. This reduces the chance of finding the same combination in someone else to in the order of 0.3 millionths of a million – in other words, negligible.

If DNA from cell nuclei is not available, or if the samples are old or in poor condition, DNA from mitochondria, tiny subunits within cells, may be used. Mitochondrial DNA is more plentiful and less prone to damage than nuclear DNA, but it is less precise because it is passed down solely from the mother's egg cell.

Genetic profiling is now put to many different uses. It can be used to identify suspects in a variety of crimes, or the victims of natural catastrophes. Palaeontologists explore the secrets of ancient DNA, and lawyers call on genetic evidence to settle paternity suits. The number of innocent people freed from prison, sometimes after serving many years of a sentence, and of guilty individuals brought to justice by genetic fingerprinting, is already beyond counting.

MYSTERIES SOLVED

Among other celebrated cases, DNA profiling has been used to identify the remains of Russia's ruling Romanov family, to disprove the royal paternity of a supposed son of France's executed King Louis XVI, and to confirm the death of the Nazi doctor Josef Mengele in Brazil in 1979.

Polymerase chain reaction 1985

Polymerase chain reaction (PCR) has become one of the most utilised techniques in biology. It enables scientists to obtain millions of copies of a specific segment of DNA – a gene, for example – in a matter of hours, even when starting from minute initial quantities. The originator of the method was Kary Mullis, an American biochemist. At the time of the discovery, Mullis was working for the Californian biotechnology firm Cetus, fabricating sequences of nucleotides (the four bases of DNA, labelled A, T, G and C) in order to detect mutations. It was a fiddly task, and he was keen to make it easier. His discovery of PCR, which he first published in 1985, won him the 1993 Nobel prize for chemistry.

Sequenced strands of DNA

PCR involves making a series of copies of given sequences of DNA. First, the DNA sample is 'denatured' – that is, separated into its two strands, each complementary to the other and oriented head to tail – by brief exposure to a relatively high temperature in a process known as DNA melting. Two primers (short DNA sequences) are then added, each one selected to fix onto either end of one of the strands of the DNA to which it is complementary. Substantial quantities of the A,T, G and C nucleotides, plus an enzyme – the polymerase – then go into the mix, which is subjected to repeated heating and cooling, causing the DNA strands to naturally align themselves. The polymerase then 'reads' each one, creating complementary sequences by adding nucleotides in the correct order. If the process is allowed to continue and more melted DNA is added, the polymerase starts to read the copy rather than the original DNA strand, then the copy of the copy and so on exponentially. Within a few cycles it is no longer copying all of the DNA, only the section between the two primers, thereby amplifying the target area. Today the process has been completely automated (see box below).

Bacterial boon
Taq polymerase (above, in blue), derived from the heat-resistant bacteria Thermis aquaticus, *is often used in PCR operations because of its resistance to high temperatures. Right: A technician at work in a virology laboratory.*

FROM THE ABYSS TO THE TEST TUBE

The different steps of PCR take place at temperatures between 45° and 95°C. But polymerases, like all enzymes, are quickly destroyed by heat, and in the early days of the process it was necessary to add fresh enzymes at the start of each cycle. In the late 1970s, though, bacteria had been discovered living around volcanic smoke-holes in the abyssal depths of the oceans. Thermostable polymerases that were resistant to high temperatures and pressures were isolated from these bacteria, making it possible to automate the process completely.

Desktop publishing 1985

At the start of the 1980s significant progress in computer graphics paved the way for some new IT applications, among them desktop publishing (DTP). Following the introduction of the Macintosh computer in 1984, *Ready, Set, Go!* software created for Apple by Manhattan Graphics made it possible to lay out documents on screen, combining text and images. At the same time the concept of WYSIWYG ('What You See Is What You Get') was established, guaranteeing that the layout on screen was essentially the same as what would appear on the printed page.

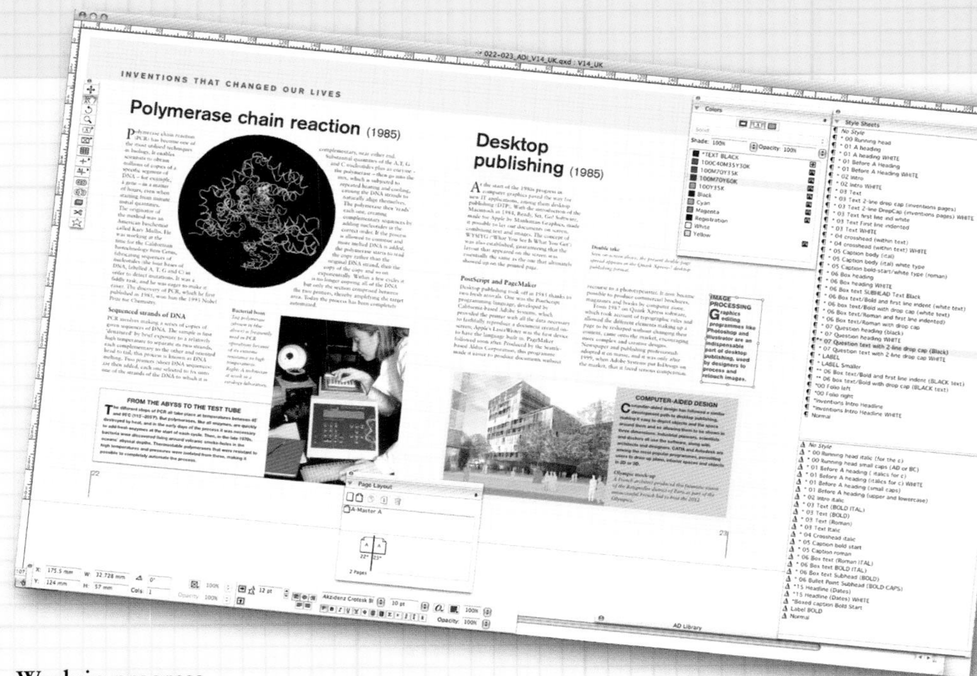

Work in progress
The on-screen version of this double-page spread as it looked in QuarkXpress-7 shortly before final changes were made.

PostScript and PageMaker

Desktop publishing took off in 1985 thanks to two fresh arrivals. One was the PostScript programming language, developed by California-based Adobe Systems, which gave the printer all the data necessary to reproduce an on-screen document on the printed page. Apple's LaserWriter was the first device to have PostScript built in. Soon afterwards, the Seattle-based Aldus Corporation launched its PageMaker program, which made it easier to produce documents without using a professional phototypesetter. It was now possible to produce commercial brochures, magazines and books by computer alone.

In 1987 QuarkXpress software took DTP into the professional sphere, enabling users to incorporate typographic rules and reshape the different elements of a page on screen. The new software encouraged more creative designs and it was adopted by designers and editors throughout the publishing world. It would be 1999 before a serious competitor to Quark emerged in the shape of Adobe System's InDesign.

IMAGE PROCESSING

Graphics editing programs like Photoshop and Illustrator are an indispensable part of desktop publishing, used by designers to process and retouch images.

COMPUTER-AIDED DESIGN

Computer-aided design (CAD) programs make it easy to depict objects and the space around them so they can be shown in three dimensions. CAD has followed a similar development path to that of desktop publishing. CATIA and Autodesk are among the most popular programs, permitting users to draw up plans, interior spaces and objects in 2D or 3D. Initially taken up by architects and designers, CAD software is now also used by industrial planners, scientists and doctors.

Olympic mock-up
This projected vision of the Batignolles district of northern Paris was produced by a French architect as part of the unsuccessful bid to host the 2012 Olympic Games in Paris.

VIDEO GAMES – 1985

Super Mario Bros, saviour of the games market

In 1985 Nintendo launched a new home video game console in the USA, the biggest game market in the world. With it came *Super Mario Bros,* a new game featuring an unlikely hero in the shape of Mario the plumber. Almost single-handedly, Mario rescued the video-game industry from the floor, becoming the best-selling game for the next two decades and launching Nintendo into the first rank of video game and console providers.

Unlikely hero
Mario on his mission to rescue Princess Toadstool and on the way to selling 40 million games.

The video game adventure had got underway as far back as 1958. In that year a US physicist named Willy Higginbotham improvised a table-tennis-themed game on an oscilloscope screen to amuse his colleagues. His *Tennis for Two* can lay claim to being the world's first video game. Three years later, students at the Massachusetts Institute of Technology (MIT) created *Spacewar* to show off the calculating powers of a new computer, the PDP-1. The game came to the attention of an American businessman, Nolan Bushnell, who adapted it for coin-operated machines comprising a screen, control levers and buttons. A first generation of the devices were installed in public places in the early 1970s, initiating the arcade-game industry.

One of the first arcade games was *Pong*, developed shortly before by the US electronics company Magnavox and commercialised by Bushnell. It turned into a worldwide success. Bushnell set up Atari in 1972, selling almost 35,000 games cabinets in the USA alone. A colour version was released in the early 1980s, proving a serious competitor for table football and bar billiards, especially with young people. Another

MULTIMEDIA CONSOLES

Sega produced a CD add-on for its Mega Drive console in the early 1990s, and the original Sony PlayStation, launched in Japan in 1994, could read and play compact discs, as could the subsequent Sega Dreamcast. With this development, consoles morphed into multimedia tools, supporting not just video games but also audio CDs, DVDs and HD (high-definition) discs.

pioneering game, *Pac-Man*, was developed in Japan and launched in 1980, reaching the USA the same year. The player controlled a pizza-shaped 'creature' as it swallowed up dots in an electronic maze, all the while dodging enemies, or 'ghosts', which it destroyed by eating them. The game became hugely popular, even spawning an animated TV series.

Temporary blip

At the time, Atari was firmly established as the leading player in a market that came to be worth over $5 billion in the USA alone. Between 1976 and 1980 Atari's earnings grew by a factor of 25. This golden age of arcade games coincided with the launch of the first home consoles: the Odyssey (1972), the Atari 2600 (1977), the Philips Videopac (1979), Mattel's Intellivision (1980), Coleco's ColecoVision (1982) and Smith Engineering's Vectrex (1983), among others. But despite the proliferation of consoles, few genuinely new and original games were released. As a result the public's interest waned, leading to a collapse of the video-game market in 1983. But at the same time, more households were becoming equipped with computers. Video games, delivered on cassettes that took an age to install, could be played on new machines such as the Apple II, the Sinclair ZX80, the Commodore 64 or the Amstrad CPC. All that was needed was an exciting new game to reignite the market. It arrived in 1985 in the shape of Nintendo's *Super Mario Bros.*

A new era dawns

Super Mario Bros was designed for the NES console. This was challenged by Sega's Master System from 1987 on, while the Amiga and Atari ST took off in the microcomputer field. They provided enough computing power to allow sophisticated graphics to replace the squared-off silhouettes and bent-wire figures of earlier machines. Capacity would double again after 1990 with the introduction of the Sega Megadrive and Super Nintendo.

Encouraged by its experience in the 1980s with Game & Watch, a line of inexpensive games designed for a handheld console, Nintendo launched the Game Boy in 1990. Operating initially in black and white, the device was the size of a paperback book and came bundled with Tetris, an addictive, block-stacking puzzle game developed in 1985 by a Russian

Worldwide phenomena
Pac-Man (far left), created by Japan's Toru Iwatani, invaded the world's amusement arcades in the 1980s and became one of the most popular and longest-running video games of all time. Below: a Super Mario console.

Collectors' items
The Atari console (top left) dates from about 1977. The Game Boy (above) is more recent, being launched in Japan in 1989. It came with a black-and-white screen to keep costs down.

MULTITASKER

Nintendo began life as a maker of playing cards in 1889. The company started marketing toys in the 1960s, but it also sold instant rice and even ran a taxi company before finding its niche in video games.

Passionate fans
Above: Two of the lucky individuals who got to test-drive an early version of Gran Turismo 5 *at the SEMA Show in Las Vegas in 2007. Left: The joystick for Sony's PlayStation. Below: Crowds keen to get their hands on the new PlayStation 2 at the launch in 2002.*

engineer, Alexei Pajitnov. More than 100 million Game Boys were eventually sold, as children and adolescents around the world were consumed by the new passion.

Not just for kids

By the 1990s video games were also attracting an adult audience. In 1992 *Alone in the Dark*, inspired by the dark novels of American author H.P. Lovecraft, unleashed the survival horror genre, in which the gamer has to escape from a dangerous and terrifying world. A year later *Doom*, a bloodthirsty shoot-em-up game, signalled a swing towards gore. Then in 1996 Lara Croft made her first appearance as the heroine of *Tomb Raider*. Athletic, intrepid, sexy and intelligent, Lara became a fantasy icon for a whole generation of adolescents, a virtual-reality star who spawned a host of spin-offs.

In 1977 the release of *Grand Theft Auto* and *Carmageddon* sparked fierce criticism of the industry, with some countries banning both games. The gangster protagonist of the former has to win his stripes in an underworld milieu, while the latter stages a blood-stained race through city streets with bonuses for killing pedestrians. Video games were accused of a variety of evils, from making gamers violent, stupid or epileptic to causing physical addiction in a similar way to drugs.

PlayStation, Wii and DS

The public appetite for games was undimmed. In the late 1990s, home consoles were adapted to host online gaming, encouraged at the time by the explosive growth of Internet use. Titles like *World of Warcraft*, launched in 1994, saw video games go global, with large numbers of players participating at the same time; it was now possible for gamers to interact with other players located anywhere in the world. Up to this time the gaming world had been overwhelmingly male, but now growing numbers of women were attracted by series like *The Sims*.

With the arrival of Xbox 360 in 2005 and PlayStation 3 the following year, computer graphics became startlingly lifelike. Meanwhile, games were driving the demand for ever-more powerful home computers. Titles were now

ANOTHER WORLD ON-SCREEN

Three-dimensional virtual worlds started to appear in the mid 1990s. Accessed with the aid of software via the Internet, they allow players to assume on-screen avatars that can evolve and interact with others. *Second Life* (left), originally released in 2003, creates an entire social universe for its users, with its own currency that can be converted into real-life money. A whole parallel economy has developed in these metaverses (as virtual worlds are also called), where players can do their shopping, go to nightclubs and take in shows. Businesses use them to test and sell new products and to conduct job interviews. *Second Life* also provides a platform for conferences, courses, exhibitions and film previews.

Getting real
The original Lara Croft (below), adventurer and archaeologist on the track of lost treasures. She took on real human form in two feature films released in 2001 and 2003, played by the actress Angelina Jolie.

developed by elite teams and launched with professional campaigns – with good reason as the market was expanding by 20 per cent a year, approaching £30 billion in the EU by 2008.

Always seeking to make its products more user-friendly, Nintendo launched the Wii home console and the portable DS in 2006. The Wii has a wireless remote that can detect movement in three dimensions, so using it no longer means sitting on a sofa but standing up in the middle of the room. The DS has a touch-sensitive screen supporting a variety of games, some of them with educational content, from exercises to speed up reflexes or improve memory to language-learning software. This new approach aims to appeal to all the family.

Today's video-game market responds rapidly to technological developments. Sony's *EyePet*, designed for PlayStation 3, represents a first step into augmented reality: an in-built camera surveys its surroundings so the game's protagonist, a small, furry creature, can interact with the gamer. Future titles will move into three dimensions. Also in the future control levers and joysticks look set to disappear: Emotiv System and NeuroSky are already working on a helmet that can detect and interpret brain signals, with the aim of creating games controlled by thought.

THE COMING OF E-SPORTS

Established in 1997, the Cyberathlete Professional League organised the first international video-game tournament that same year, with some 300 gamers taking part online. The LAN party movement (LAN stands for Local Area Network) quickly gathered momentum, paving the way for the development of e-sports (short for 'electronic sports'). Today the top players are professionals coached by trainers, backed by managers and financed by sponsors. The winners of some tournaments can pocket hundreds of thousands of dollars.

Lifelike creatures from a digital world

In 1993 the dinosaurs of *Jurassic Park* were unleashed on expectant audiences in cinemas around the world. For once the hype was justified and the film-going public was thrilled. The images were digital, but the creatures on screen were genuinely convincing – almost as real as nature itself. Even in close-up shots the dinosaurs' digital origins could barely be detected.

The past brought back to life
The creatures of Jurassic Park *were made in the Stan Winston Studio in California. Each began life as a resin model (below), which was then used to create a 3-D computer image that was animated and given a suitable background. The scariest re-creation was the velociraptor (right), a fearsome Late Cretaceous hunter from around 70 million years ago.*

The story behind this technical triumph got underway in 1963 when Ivan Sutherland, a computer expert at the Massachusetts Institute of Technology (MIT), first developed the Sketchpad program, which allowed users to draw simple designs with a light pen. Soon afterwards the University of Utah took up the initiative, becoming the seedbed of digital imaging. There, at the start of the 1970s, Bui Tuong Phong from Vietnam and a Frenchman, Henri Gouraud, came up with algorithms to calculate shadow effects. And there too, in 1974, American Edwin Catmull, who would go on to run Pixar Studios, perfected a technique for adding surface texture to virtual-reality images. The work of these three men jointly laid the foundations for the development of computer graphics.

Low-key beginnings

Cinema and the advertising industry soon took an interest in this new way of creating visual effects. In 1973 the futuristic thriller *Westworld* included a short digital sequence. Thereafter a number of design studios set to work in the USA and Europe. SIGGRAPH (short for Special Interest Group on Graphics and Interactive Techniques) was established to serve as a forum for people working in the field, and by the early 21st century its conferences were attracting 30,000 visitors annually, along with some 250 businesses.

In the 1980s great strides forward were made in digital-imaging technology as

THREE STEPS TO A DIGITAL IMAGE

There are three steps in the creation of a digital image. First comes 3-D modelling, which involves representing the virtual object, location or character in the form of simple geometric shapes – the more there are, the better the quality of the final image will be. Next comes the finishing, which consists first of giving the shapes an appropriate surface texture – skin, wood, metal, plastic or whatever – and then adding in shading to depict shadows and desired light effects. Third, if the images are to be animated, the creator must write into a software program the parameters that define exactly how the various elements – human limbs, moving vehicles or other objects – should move.

Creating a virtual world
The special-effects animators on the 1982 film Tron *(right) spent long hours at their computers – the more so because the computer mouse was little used at the time and commands were typed in using keyboards.*

computers became more powerful and less expensive. The public first really became aware of the progress being made when the film *Tron* opened in 1982. This featured elaborate graphic effects to tell the story of a man trapped inside a video game. Walt Disney Pictures had put five animation studios and $20 million into the project. Yet however spectacular the visuals were from a technical point of view, they remained limited in their quality, and the public response was no better than lukewarm.

Simulators for the military

The US army meanwhile began putting digital imaging to use in a variety of simulators imitating fighter aircraft, submarines and tanks. In devices replicating cockpits or command hatches, with screens showing targets to hit and obstacles to overcome, military personnel could rehearse complex steering and firing manoeuvres. Officers were encouraged to improve their decision-making skills with the help of tactical simulators that provided varying terrain and weather conditions and could also change other factors such as the composition of the opposing forces, the mission objectives and the weaponry available. In 1984 NASA similarly found a use for the new technology in its VIVED (Virtual Visual Environment Display) program, intended to prepare astronauts for future space missions. This involved a helmet linked to screens showing digital images.

VIRTUAL REALITY ACCESSORIES

The earliest machines designed to immerse spectators in a virtual world pre-dated the birth of digital imagery. The first, patented in 1962, was Sensorama, the brainchild of US cinematographer Morton Heilig. It featured a one-person projection cabin in which viewers sat on a vibrating seat, experiencing the sensations of riding through Brooklyn on a motorcycle: besides the visual imagery, they could feel wind in their faces as they took in the sounds and smells of the city. In 1968 Ivan Sutherland, an MIT-trained computer scientist, produced the first head-mounted virtual-display system, called the 'Sword of Damocles'; similar devices would one day be used to teach NASA astronauts to navigate (below). Frederick Brooks, a computer scientist at the University of North Carolina, developed a 3-D touch-enabled modelling arm that blocked (or at least hindered) movement when the user came into contact with a virtual object. In about 1985 NASA added gloves to its space simulation equipment (left), permitting the wearer to manipulate virtual objects. Today there are even flak jackets equipped with air pockets that inflate rapidly to simulate the effect of bullet hits.

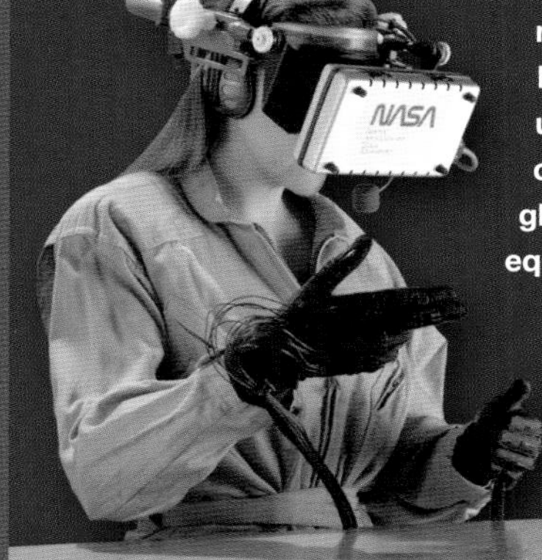

DIGITAL IMAGERY MOVES INTO ADVERTISING

Digital images made their advertising debut in the 1980s, when diagrams began cropping up in TV commercials demonstrating the efficacy of toothpastes or washing powders by showing the results close up. Over the ensuing decade a fresh application was found as digital imaging was used to incorporate sponsors' names and logos into real-life objects. In 1994 a promotion for Aquila beer in Spain was reused in northern Europe with the Amstel brandname substituted. Similar techniques have also frequently been put to use at televised sporting events.

Representing ancient and modern
Computer graphics can be used to show buildings as they might have been – this example is Angkor Wat in Cambodia (above) – or to envisage projects still on the drawing-board, like this extension to the Roland Garros Stadium in Paris proposed in 2009 (top left).

Space medicine
NASA technicians produced this 3-D computer model of the elements of the inner ear (above) to analyse what happens to people's sense of balance when in space.

A multi-purpose tool

Even so, until well into the 1990s digital imaging was associated primarily with video games, films (particularly3-D credit sequences), advertising and weather reports featuring maps employing computer graphics. But the technical progress made in modelling as well as in simulation was increasingly attracting the attention of big business, especially in the ship-building, aeronautic and motor industries, where digital images came to play a vital part in the design and development of components and prototypes. In similar fashion, computer graphics allowed architects and urban planners to visualise projected developments while they were still in the ideas stage. They could simulate the experience of moving around inside buildings, or orient the structures in different ways in order to maximise their exposure to sunlight.

Historians used digital imaging to reconstruct ruins, showing ancient edifices as they might have appeared when they were still in use. Doctors made increasing use of the new tool to design customised prosthetic limbs.

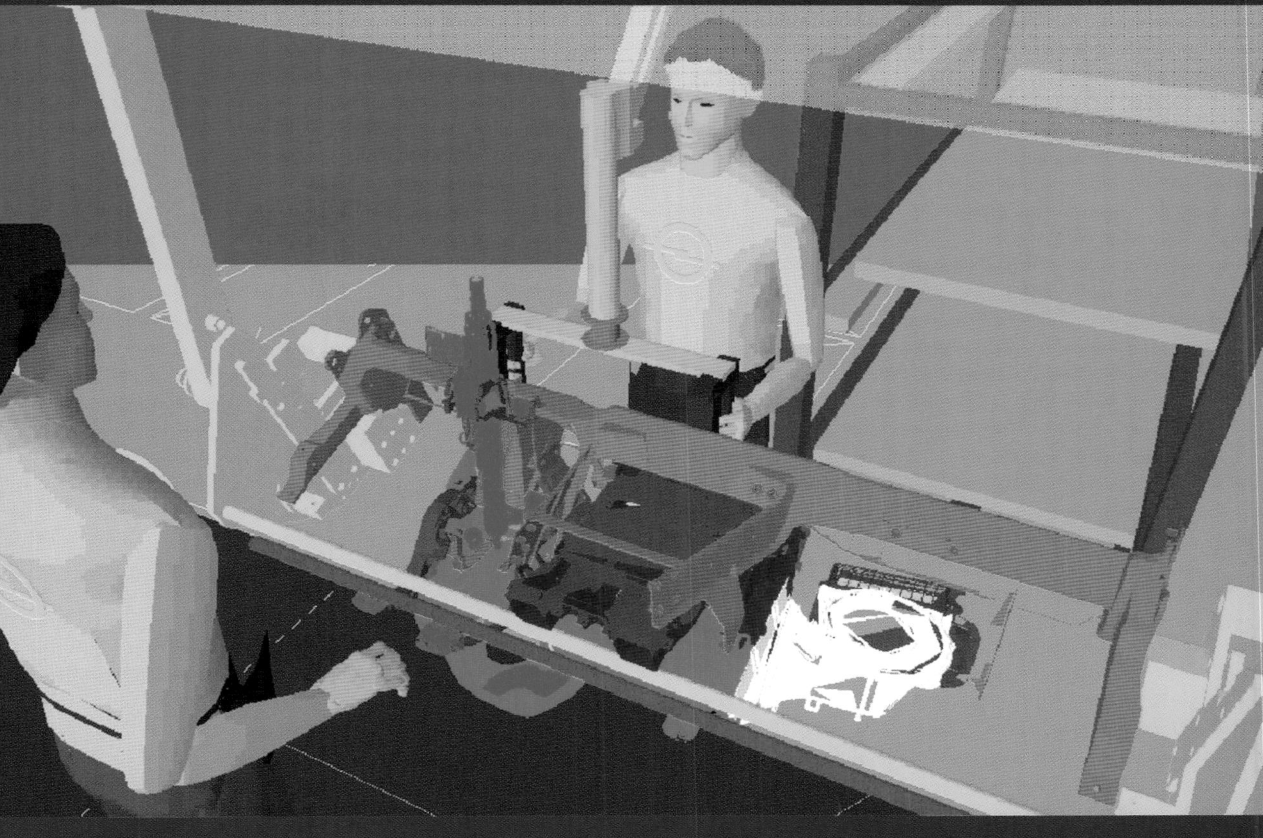

Methods engineering
3-D computer modelling can be use to improve ergonomics in the workplace. Here (right), the technique is used to test out and optimise the layout of a work-station in a car factory.

Groundbreaking image
In 1975 a virtual teapot (bottom right), designed at the University of Utah, became the first digitised image to be convincingly modelled in the round. The real-life pot that resulted is preserved in the Computer History Museum in Mountain View, California.

Also in the medical world, images of organs obtained by magnetic resonance could be digitised then manipulated to observe them from different angles to aid diagnosis. Digital images came to be used in physics research laboratories, for example to model quantum phenomena or atomic fission. In chemistry they were used to study the interaction of molecules, and in biology to observe the configuration of proteins. Meteorologists looked to them to replicate the movement of air masses, economists to chart the rise and decline of currencies. In the social sciences they reproduced the movement of crowds or propagation of languages or ideas.

Conquering the big screen

Meanwhile digital imaging was continuing to make inroads in the film industry. In 1988 *Willow* introduced the public to morphing – transforming one image into another through a seamless progression of tiny alterations. By the early 21st century the technique was being used by police forces to simulate ageing; one application was to show what children who had been missing for many years might look like in the present day.

In 1989 the Canadian film director James Cameron included a moving encounter between a real actress and a digital extra-terrestrial in the film *The Abyss*. In *Terminator 2* a robot made of liquid metal was able to take on any shape. Steven Spielberg took a huge step forward in 1993 with the dinosaurs of *Jurassic Park*, digital animations which for the very first time looked entirely natural. The following year saw the release of *Forrest Gump*, in which Tom Hanks is seen chatting and shaking hands with President John F. Kennedy, who had died 30 years earlier. The illusion was complete: thanks to digital animation and sound manipulation, Kennedy spoke in his familiar tones, and his mouth movements were shaped to match the words he was speaking.

Almost anything now became possible. Images, whether animated or photographed, could be retouched, manipulated or even completely fabricated. In the cinema these techniques were variously used to multiply groups of characters to create a crowd or even an army (as in *Braveheart* in 1995); to reconstruct the interior of a castle (in the 1996 German film *The Ogre*); and, in *Babe*, to give animals human speech and characteristics. The release of *Toy Story* in 1995 broke new ground as the entire film was made by digital imaging, opening the way for other films of the same kind.

ASIA GOES DIGITAL

In 1995 the market for virtual reality was essentially limited to the USA and Europe, and amounted globally to about $135 million. Five years later, after Asia had joined in, the total value of sales had soared to more than $1 billion.

Reality sandwich
Madonna (above) on screen with members of the virtual group Gorillaz at the 2006 Grammy Awards ceremony. After the performance she appeared at the awards in person.

Stunningly realistic

Digital imaging also gave birth to Gorillaz, a virtual band created by ex-Blur musician Damon Albarn. The band members appear in the form of virtual-reality avatars. In some parts of the world, the technique has even been put to use in courts of law to reconstruct crime scenes, helping jurors to better understand the sequence of events involved. The last remaining bastion now seemed to be the creation of virtual human beings in a convincingly realistic manner.

In 2005 Weta Digital achieved a technical *tour de force* in re-creating the character of Gollum for New Zealander Peter Jackson in his adaptation of J.R.R. Tolkien's *Lord of the Rings*. Retouched in post-production, the images were almost perfect. James Cameron went even further in his 2009 hit *Avatar*, using high-definition cameras to record actors' faces in close-up, then employing the wrinkles and pores as a natural grid for software to create incredibly realistic facial movements. The next step will be to achieve the same results using real-time imagery.

Rotoscoped and realistic
Gollum, one of the most memorable characters from J.R.R. Tolkien's Lord of the Rings, *as digitised for the film version by the New Zealand-based special-effects company, Weta Digital. The firm also worked on realistic 3-D crowd effects for the battle scenes.*

A NEW KIND OF ACTING

Film actors have had to learn to adjust to digital imagery. The cast of the 1999 *Star Wars* film, *The Phantom Menace*, had to get used to interacting with a virtual character. In *The Polar Express* (2004), *Monster House* (2006) and *Beowulf* (2007), cast members were covered in sensor chips that registered their movements, which were then replicated by their digital avatars. The human players thereby became little more than support mechanisms designed to give the artificial images the realism they otherwise still lacked. The practice raises the question of whether actors might one day become entirely redundant, replaced by virtual-reality clones.

IMAX 3-D 1986

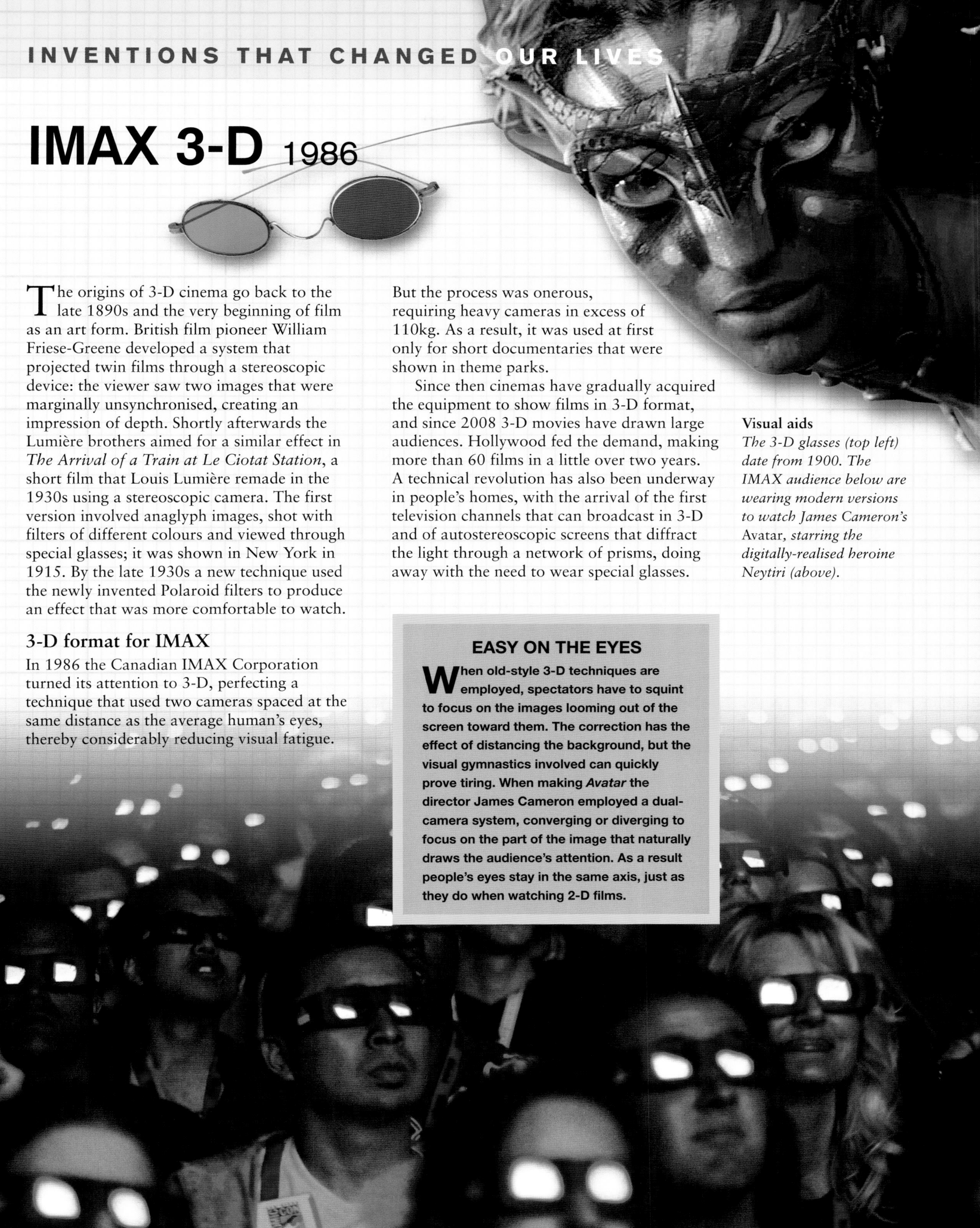

The origins of 3-D cinema go back to the late 1890s and the very beginning of film as an art form. British film pioneer William Friese-Greene developed a system that projected twin films through a stereoscopic device: the viewer saw two images that were marginally unsynchronised, creating an impression of depth. Shortly afterwards the Lumière brothers aimed for a similar effect in *The Arrival of a Train at Le Ciotat Station*, a short film that Louis Lumière remade in the 1930s using a stereoscopic camera. The first version involved anaglyph images, shot with filters of different colours and viewed through special glasses; it was shown in New York in 1915. By the late 1930s a new technique used the newly invented Polaroid filters to produce an effect that was more comfortable to watch.

3-D format for IMAX

In 1986 the Canadian IMAX Corporation turned its attention to 3-D, perfecting a technique that used two cameras spaced at the same distance as the average human's eyes, thereby considerably reducing visual fatigue. But the process was onerous, requiring heavy cameras in excess of 110kg. As a result, it was used at first only for short documentaries that were shown in theme parks.

Since then cinemas have gradually acquired the equipment to show films in 3-D format, and since 2008 3-D movies have drawn large audiences. Hollywood fed the demand, making more than 60 films in a little over two years. A technical revolution has also been underway in people's homes, with the arrival of the first television channels that can broadcast in 3-D and of autostereoscopic screens that diffract the light through a network of prisms, doing away with the need to wear special glasses.

Visual aids
The 3-D glasses (top left) date from 1900. The IMAX audience below are wearing modern versions to watch James Cameron's Avatar, *starring the digitally-realised heroine Neytiri (above).*

EASY ON THE EYES

When old-style 3-D techniques are employed, spectators have to squint to focus on the images looming out of the screen toward them. The correction has the effect of distancing the background, but the visual gymnastics involved can quickly prove tiring. When making *Avatar* the director James Cameron employed a dual-camera system, converging or diverging to focus on the part of the image that naturally draws the audience's attention. As a result people's eyes stay in the same axis, just as they do when watching 2-D films.

Personal digital assistants 1986

As IT equipment grew smaller, computer manufacturers set about developing pocket-sized devices for use as personal organisers, combining a diary, address book and notepad. Initially known as palmtop computers, they are now usually called PDAs (Personal Digital Assistants), a term coined by John Sculley, CEO of Apple. The idea caught on with business customers, largely thanks to the Organiser II released by the British firm Psion in 1986. Hardly bigger than a calculator, it had a screen with room for four lines of text and sufficient memory to support a diary and small database. The PDA had arrived, but was the wider world ready for it?

Difficult beginnings

In 1993 Apple unveiled the Newton – its full title was the Newton MessagePad. The stylus and touch-sensitive screen were designed to appeal to people used to drawing up plans and totting up figures, but the device had its drawbacks. At 400g it was too heavy, the handwriting function was not up to scratch and it cost too much, all of which added up to the Newton being a commercial failure. Rival devices arrived on the market around the same time, including the Casio Zoomer and offerings from Hewlett Packard and Sharp, but still demand failed to take off.

In 1995 the US firm Palm Computing launched the Palm Pilot, and the PDA finally came into its own. Conceived by Jeff Hawkins, the device was small, light (about 120g) and easy to use. In effect, it became a mobile extension of the office computer, rapidly establishing itself as the industry standard: the first million units sold in just 18 months. Four years later the Handspring Visor opened the way to multimedia PDAs, and in the early 2000s the devices converged with telephone technology to create the first smartphones.

Personal helper
Many people have come to regard their PDA as indispensable. It can be consulted anywhere (left), any time, providing a mini-version of office tools such as a diary and a word-processor. The multimedia function enables users to watch videos and listen to music in MP3 format. Top: the Apple Newton.

CUSTOMISED OPERATING SYSTEMS

PDAs need an operating system (OS), just like larger computers, and these vary from one manufacturer to another. Apple's Newton was equipped with Newton OS. The most popular are Palm Computing's Palm OS and Microsoft's Windows Mobile, also known as the Pocket PC format. Some PDAs can function with Linux.

Stereolithography 1986

Stereolithography makes it possible to construct three-dimensional objects from two-dimensional images, which can be photographs or digital designs. A computer scans the image, using software that deconstructs it into virtual slices each covering a thickness of about 0.07mm. A laser then transcribes the dimensions onto a block of light-sensitive resin, which cures and hardens on contact, reproducing the proportions of the original object. To get a full 3-D effect, the other side must be treated in the same way.

Patented in March 1986 by American inventor Charles W. Hull, the founder of 3D Systems, stereolithography is now widely employed in industry. Other uses include making copies of archaeological discoveries, and it also offers a quick way of making busts of living people.

Blow-up
A 3-D rendering of the inner ear of a 2.8-million-year-old fossil baboon (right). The size has been boosted ten-fold, from the original 2cm to 22cm.

First step
In the first stage of the process, a computer scans and analyses the subject – here a young woman's head.

Radio data system 1987

Developed out of a German system for delivering up-to-date traffic information, the Radio Data System (RDS) is a communication standard that allows small amounts of text to be transmitted digitally along with FM radio broadcasts. Originally intended to make it easier to listen to car radios by automatically scanning frequencies, the RDS now carries a variety of messages, typically including time signals, traffic news and the name of the station currently on air. A Finn, Kari Ilmonen, and France's André Keller were responsible for adapting RDS from the German traffic information system (known as ARI) from 1974 on. RDS arrived in Britain in 1988, by which time it had already been deployed in Austria, Belgium, Denmark, Germany, France and Italy; the Netherlands, Portugal and Switzerland followed soon after. Today, 200 million RDS-enabled car radios are produced around the world every year.

EON

Developed from 1991 on by the major car-radio manufacturers, the EON (Enhanced Other Networks) system now forms part of RDS. It interrupts radio reception or a CD that is playing to give drivers traffic information flashes.

SUPERCONDUCTORS – 1986

Transmitting electricity without leakage

In 1986 Alex Müller and Georg Bednorz, working at IBM's laboratory at Rüschlikon in Switzerland, demonstrated that a ceramic material made of oxides of copper, lanthanum and barium became superconductive at –243°C. Their discovery launched a new class of superconductors.

The Meissner-Ochsenfeld effect
A magnet levitates above a superconductor kept at a very low temperature.

Superconductivity occurs when a material provides zero resistance to the passage of an electric current. It was discovered by chance in 1911 by a Dutch physicist, Heike Kamerlingh Onnes, while studying mercury: cooled in liquid helium to –269°C, the metal lost all of its electrical resistance. The discovery was f fundamental importance for understanding the workings of the universe, but had few practical applications at the time given that the critical temperature at which the phenomenon of superconductivity became apparent was so close to absolute zero (–273.15°C).

In 1933 two German scientists, Walther Meissner and Robert Ochsenfeld, discovered that superconductors expel magnetic fields; surreal images of a magnet floating above a superconductor subsequently received widespread publicity. In 1956 three American researchers – John Bardeen, Leon Cooper and John Schrieffer – published the so-called BCS theory (named from their initials) to explain the phenomenon. Yet for the discovery to

NUCLEAR CONFINEMENT

Tokamaks are particle accelerators inside which nuclear fusion reactions analogous to those produced within stars can take place. For that to happen, jets of particles have to circulate at incredibly high temperatures of several million degrees Centigrade that no known material could withstand, making it crucial that the particle beam should never come into contact with the walls of the reactor. To achieve this, scientists use a technique known as magnetic confinement: the beam is remotely controlled by a magnetic field created by superconducting electromagnets – the only magnets powerful enough to do the job.

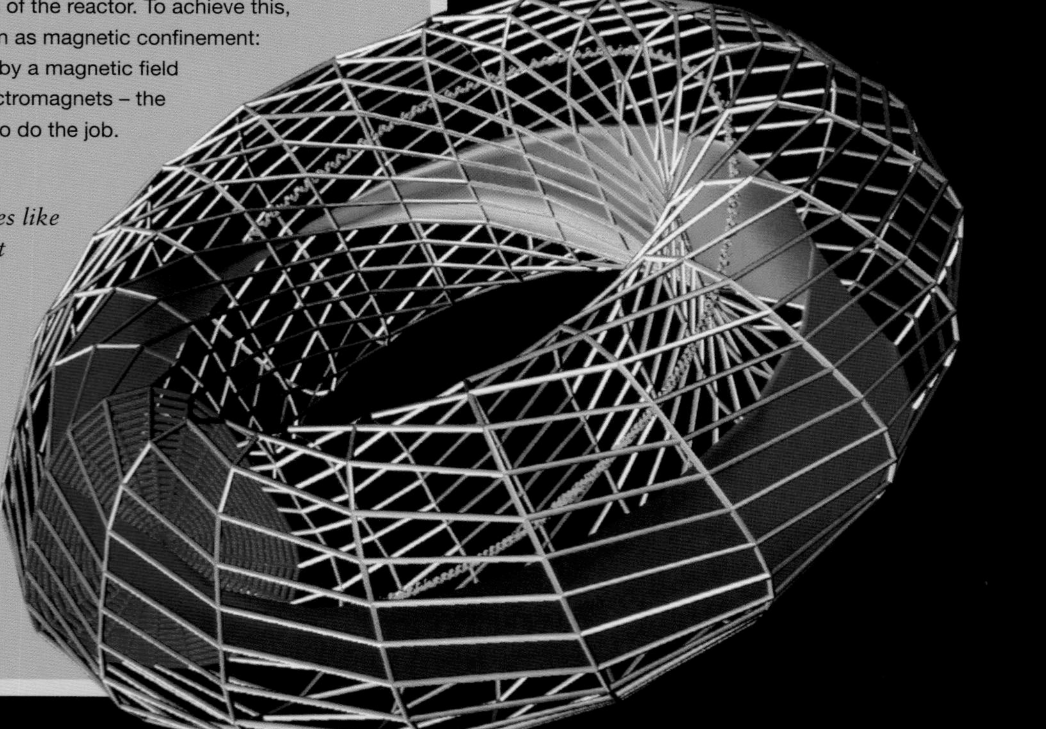

A magnetic cage
In a Tokamak reactor, particles like the ion shown here as a bright yellow band are held within an electromagnetic field (represented by the coloured grid), which controls their trajectory within the ring-shaped, hollow reactor. Devices of this type are indispensable for studying phenomena associated with nuclear fusion, potentially an almost limitless energy source of the future.

The Compact Muon Solenoid *A giant particle detector, the CMS forms part of the Large Hadron Collider near Geneva.*

have practical applications, superconductivity had to occur at more realistic temperatures.

Getting warmer

The breakthrough by Alex Müller and Georg Bednorz, demonstrating superconductivity at –243°C, showed that the phenomenon was possible at warmer temperatures. The new class of superconductors launched as a result were known as the cuprates because they contained copper (*cuprum* in Latin). The hunt was on for materials with higher critical temperatures, with Japanese researchers at the forefront.

In 1988 a thallium–barium compound was discovered with a transition temperature of –188°C. This crossed an important barrier, because liquid nitrogen, which can be produced industrially at much lower cost than liquid helium, has a temperature of –196°C, so it could be used as a refrigerant to keep the new material at or below the required temperature. In 1993 two teams of French physicists, in Paris and Grenoble, announced the production of superconducting materials at temperatures approaching normal: at –23°C and –3°C respectively. However, these were only achieved with experimental samples subject to extremely high pressures. The record temperature for non-laboratory conditions is roughly –130°C.

Putting superconductors to use

As superconducting materials provide no resistance at all to electric currents, they give off no energy in the form of heat. So in industry they could, in theory, be used to produce miniaturised electrical systems without any need to worry about heat loss; invisibly thin cables could carry intense currents, and electronics components could be made ultra-rapid. Superconducting magnets generating powerful magnetic fields are already used in particle accelerators and for medical imaging within MRI scanners, as well as to levitate Japan's Maglev trains.
Yet their high cost and the need for constant liquid-nitrogen cooling, which makes them difficult to handle, has so far limited their use.

STORING ENERGY

Electrical inductors have many uses, from reducing interference and filtering electrical frequencies to lighting. They have been considered as a possible means of storing electrical energy, but their capacity has so far been limited by the resistance of the materials of which they are made. The arrival of superconductors has changed all that and researchers are working on prototype superconducting coils that can store and instantly release hundreds of thousands of joules of electrical charge.

Superconductor in close-up *In this simulation of a new superconducting ceramic (below), the red pyramids and green squares are ions of copper joined by ions of oxygen, the yellow spheres represent yttrium ions and the blue dots barium. The material's transition temperature (the temperature at which it becomes superconductive) is about –200°C.*

THE FORMATION OF STARS – 1987

How stars are born from clouds of dust

Stars are formed out of immense clouds of gas and dust within galaxies. Our own star, the Sun, was created in this way, and new stars are still being born in stellar nurseries scattered across the universe.

The matter of stars
Young stars – like the Eagle Nebula (left), some 7,000 light-years from Earth – emerge from clouds of gas and dust.

In 1987 astronomers discovered the most luminous and massive star-formation region in our galaxy, lying more than 30,000 light-years from Earth. The region, which they labelled W49A, is essentially a vast cloud of hydrogen molecules and dust, measuring some hundred light-years across. Using the Very Large Array radiotelescope resources in New Mexico and the Hat Creek Radio Observatory in California, a team of astronomers directed by James Jackson, from the University of California Berkeley campus, established that the gas cloud is collapsing in on itself. Their observations provided some of the best evidence yet to support the long-held theory that collapsing clouds of gas are at the origin of star formation.

In W49A the process has already spawned a dozen new stars and dozens more will eventually follow. The astronomers duly called such regions stellar nurseries.

Heart of a nebula
This spectactular view of the star-forming region known as W49A (above) comes from the Very Large Array radio observatory in New Mexico.

A star nursery

So how exactly does the process work? Initially the cloud is isolated within its galaxy, like a seed waiting to germinate in a clearing in a vast forest. Just as internal air pressure keeps a balloon inflated, so the pressure of the gas within the cloud stops it from collapsing in on itself under its own weight, until some violent event – perhaps a star exploding nearby and showering the cloud with rapidly-moving matter, or perhaps the approach of a second cloud – breaks the equilibrium. Whatever the cause, the cloud is destabilised by the shock. The pressure within is no longer sufficient to counterbalance the force of gravity, and it slowly starts to collapse in on itself like a burst

THE ORIGINS OF THE STAR THEORY

One of the earliest attempts to explain star formation scientifically was made in about 1630 by the philosopher René Descartes, who suggested that the Sun and planets might have emerged from a single primitive nebula that had contracted. Immanuel Kant took up the idea in 1755, proposing that the Sun might have been born in the centre while the planets formed from a ring of orbiting matter. In 1796 the French astronomer Pierre-Simon Laplace elaborated this scenario, postulating that the rotation of the nebula accelerated as it contracted, rather like a skater clutching her arms into her body as she spins. The result, he claimed, would be a ring with a dense centre, from which our Sun was formed.

Cradle of light
The star-forming region known as LH95 (above) lies in the Large Magellanic Cloud galaxy. This high-resolution image of stars there was taken by the Hubble Space Telescope.

A star is born
T Tauri in the Taurus constellation (in box, above) is still in the process of formation. The central point of light represents the heart of the star, surrounded by a ring of planetary matter from which vast jets of particles are dispersed into space.

balloon, fragmenting into ever-smaller parts whose mass ends up equivalent to that of stars. The protostellar clouds created in this way will themselves collapse in similar fashion, increasing in density as they do so. They become opaque, imprisoning the energy contained within them rather in the way that fog prevents light from escaping. Pressure and temperature rise as if in a pressure-cooker, slowing the collapse. At that point the clouds begin to emit light, becoming protostars.

The creation of planets

The protostar is still surrounded by a ring of orbiting matter left over from its formation, some of which continues to rain down upon the new star. The rest remains in orbit, subject to violent collisions that cause the matter to coalesce, forming bigger and bigger bodies, some of which eventually become planets. In the heart of the protostar, the temperature is by now high enough to trigger thermonuclear reactions that fuse the hydrogen atoms within it, giving off energy from what has by now become a nascent star surrounded by a planetary system. High winds of particles ejected from the star sweep away whatever remains of the orbiting ring of interstellar dust. Our own Sun was born in this way over the space of tens of millions of years some 4.6 billion years ago, creating a planetary system in which the necessary conditions were present for the emergence of life.

Today astronomers have powerful telescopes, located not just on the ground but also in space, from which they can observe the stages of star formation at work, from the initial clouds of hydrogen molecules through to the emergence of planets. They are still seeking to verify that the same process created the very first stars, born just a few hundred million years after the Big Bang itself, and thereby answer once and for all the question of how stars are formed.

EXPLORING ANIMAL LANGUAGE

Learning to communicate with animals

Through their ability to use sign language and symbols that stand in for words, a chimpanzee and a bonobo, named Washoe and Kanzi respectively, crossed the supposedly insuperable language barrier between human beings and animals. Humans, it seems, are not the only species capable of using complex and subtle language.

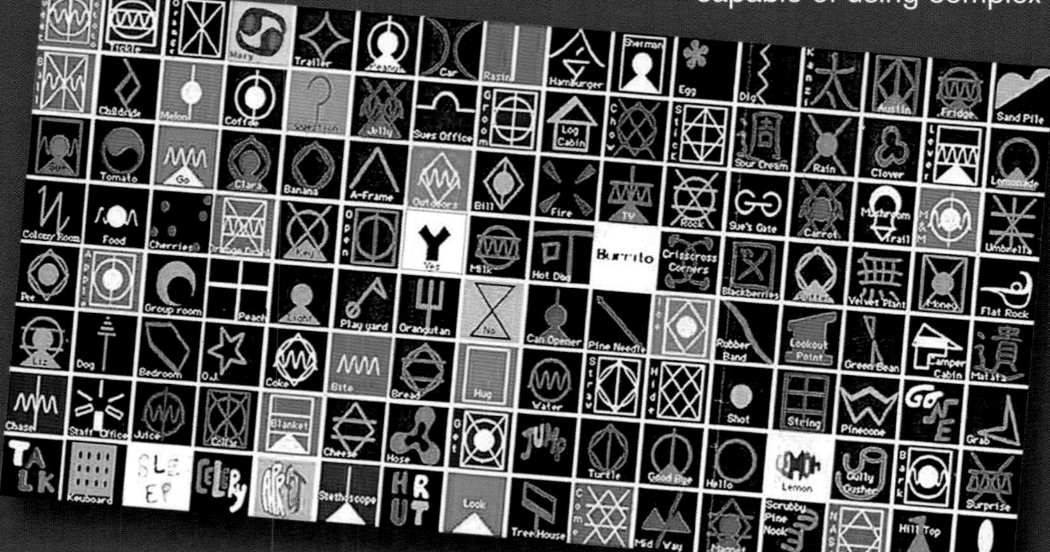

Image bank
Kanzi the bonobo uses the lexigrams shown above to express himself.

Washoe was a female chimpanzee of the *Pan troglodytes* species and the star performer at the Chimpanzee and Human Communication Institute at Central Washington University in the northwest USA. When she died in October 2007, at the age of 42, she was showered with eulogies. She had achieved a great deal: Washoe had profoundly changed the way in which humans regard other primates and, beyond that, the entire animal kingdom.

Phrase-making skills

Washoe's story begins in 1966 when two psychologists, Beatrice and Allen Gardner, began to teach her American Sign Language (ASL). She was just 10 months old at the time, having been born in West Africa. By the age of four she had mastered 130 signs, each corresponding to a word that she would use, for example, to ask for a banana. Washoe thus became the first chimpanzee to communicate with humans by means of a language made up of symbols. She went on to prove capable of combining the signs into at least 245 different

Talking with birds
Irene Pepperberg (below), a professor at Brandeis University in Boston, USA, bought Alex the parrot (perched on her finger) in 1977, when he was just one year old. By the time of his death in 2007, her work had made him internationally famous. Since then Pepperberg has continued her research with other birds, including Arthur (below, on the right).

DOLPHINS AND PARROTS TOO

As the species closest to humans, chimpanzees were an obvious first choice for researchers eager to explore the foundations of language. Yet in experiments from the 1960s on, other creatures have shown surprising evidence of sophisticated communication skills. In Hawaii, Louis Herman used a coded language involving hand and arm gestures to communicate with dolphins, which modified their behaviour appropriately when confronted with gestures indicating such concepts as 'basket', 'ball', 'left' or 'right'. A US professor named Irene Pepperberg observed a grey parrot from Gabon named Alex, who could understand a thousand words and used 150 of them in experiments testing his understanding of the shape, colour and number of objects presented to him.

phrases used for more complex requests – for example, the sequence 'you–me–go–quick' indicated she wanted to leave the laboratory.

Then, in 1979, something even more remarkable happened. Washoe adopted a young male chimpanzee, Loulis, and began teaching him ASL signs in his turn. Even though Loulis never attained the same level of understanding as his adoptive mother, the fact that she taught him at all was the real surprise. Previously it had been assumed that only humans could actively teach one another in this way; animals, it was thought, could only learn indirectly by observation.

Dissident voices

In the early 1980s some critics began to question the significance of the experiment. They claimed that the results obtained with Washoe were due to intensive training, inducing her to seek rewards in the form of play or food, and had little in common with the richness of human language, which can handle elaborate symbols and thought processes. Others focused on Washoe's supposed teaching of Loulis; some neutral observers contested the number of symbols that the young chimpanzee had really learned.

Yet Washoe's example led to other, more ambitious experiments, conducted from the 1980s on with the chimpanzees' smaller relations, the bonobos. The most gifted was a male named Kanzi, observed at the University of Georgia by Sue Savage-Rumbaugh. By the age of 30 Kanzi was operating a keyboard with 384 lexigrams – abstract symbols representing actions, objects or qualifiers. In the view of those who knew him, Kanzi's understanding of spoken English was equivalent to that of a two-and-a-half-year-old child. The experiments have real significance, indicating that human beings are not a race apart and that others in the animal kingdom share the language ability.

Student chimp
Nim Chimpsky studying sign language with a researcher at Columbia University in the USA. He was named after the American language theorist Noam Chomsky.

OBSERVING ANIMAL COMMUNICATION

Rather than teaching chimpanzees the rudiments of human language, primatologists today prefer to study animal communication in the natural environment. The signs animals use can be complex, going well beyond the familiar gestures and cries. In 1991 an ethologist working in the Ivory Coast observed a group of chimpanzees moving oddly, apparently directed by one of their number drumming on a tree trunk some distance away. More recently researchers in Ivory Coast have shown that small guenon monkeys use a primitive form of syntax, combining the 25 sounds that make up their 'vocabulary' in different sequences, depending on the context and the individual they are addressing. It has also been shown that monkeys – especially females – fractionally delay their response in communications with one another, as humans do in conversation.

Internet computer viruses 1988

Blaster, Sasser, Netsky, Mydoom ... just a few of the names given to malicious computer programs collectively referred to as viruses. All are destructive, but some can cause serious damage to the machines they infect. The first officially recognised virus was created by Fred Cohen in 1983. As a student at the University of Southern California, he designed a parasitic program that acted as a sort of digital life form capable of reproducing itself inside other computers.

The creators of early viruses mostly did it for fun or for the intellectual challenge it presented, rather than through any serious desire to do harm. That situation did not last. In 1986 two Pakistani brothers, Basit and Amjad Alvis, gave tourists copies of software infected with the Brain virus. When they returned home, the holiday-makers unwittingly passed on the contagion. Relatively inoffensive though it was, this first worm, spread via floppy disks, prevented operating systems starting up and instead showed a message inviting those affected to contact the authors for 'vaccination' against the pest. Then in 1987 the fearsome Lehigh virus showed up, which was capable of damaging the data stored on computers.

Widespread contagion

The scope of this new form of criminality was massively increased by the spread of the Internet, which allowed viruses to propagate on a global scale. In 1988 the Morris worm became the first virus to be spread in this way, paralysing an estimated 10 per cent of all computers attached to the infant Net at the time. From that point on, attacks on the system grew steadily more aggressive. Unleashed automatically or at a distance by so-called 'logic bombs', the viruses destroy files, hard discs and operating systems. E-mails are favourite vectors – in the year 2000 the famous 'Melissa' and 'I Love You' viruses were spread in this way – but mobiles and smartphones are increasingly popular targets. Effective antivirus software is the only solution to the problem.

Worm creator
Robert Tappan Morris in 1988 (below left). Morris was a student at Cornell University when he designed the worm that bears his name. He became the first hacker to be hauled before the US courts. Below: Spotting damage caused by a virus within a programming sequence.

TYPES OF MALWARE

While 'virus' is often used as a generic term for malicious software, specific forms include 'worms', which can reproduce indefinitely, and 'Trojan horses', intended to take control of the computer. 'Rootkits' are stealth devices designed to conceal a virus's presence.

The abortion pill 1988

In the late 1950s Gregory Pincus, inventor of the contraceptive pill, put forward the idea that preventing ovulation might not be the only way of stopping pregnancy. He thought it should be possible to disrupt the first stages of conception by intervening in the hormonal processes that rule them. As it turned out, a dose of hormones can indeed prevent a fertilised egg from implanting in the uterus. This principle was put to use in the 1960s to develop the first 'morning-after' pills.

In 1979 a new chapter opened when the French endocrinologist Étienne-Émile Beaulieu created mifepristone (initially known as RU 486), a synthetic steroid which is capable of neutralising progesterone. This made it possible to intervene with hormones in cases of established pregnancy: progesterone is indispensable to pregnancy, so administering an antiprogesterone can interrupt the foetal development process.

A controversial discovery

The new compound was tested in a Geneva hospital in 1981 and was provisionally judged to be a major step forward. Stopping pregnancy by ingesting a drug seemed less traumatic and also less risky than using the existing surgical method. But this in itself provoked strong reactions from opponents of abortion, who considered that the simplicity of the procedure trivialised the decision to terminate pregnancy. Anti-abortion activists organised boycotts of products made by Roussel Uclaf, the laboratories where mifepristone was produced, and the firm's directors even received death threats.

Even so, in 1988 the mifepristone abortion pill was authorised for use in France and China; Britain and Sweden followed suit in the early 1990s. From 1999 on, the use of the abortion pill spread widely across Europe and to the USA, then gradually to other countries where abortion is legal.

Conflicting views
Supporters of the abortion pill (top) and opponents (above) demonstrating in Houston, Texas, in August 1992.

MORNING-AFTER PILLS AND ABORTION PILLS

Taken within 72 hours of unprotected sex, the morning-after pill hinders fertilisation and the fixing of the egg in the uterus. If that stage has already taken place, the morning-after pill cannot prevent the progress of the pregnancy. In contrast, the anti-progesterone properties of mifepristone in the abortion pill cause uterine mucus to detach, expelling the embryo just as in a miscarriage. It is normally used in the first seven weeks of pregnancy.

MULTIPLE USES

Although most terminations in the UK are still performed surgically, the chemical alternative is now often offered to women considering abortion. Mifepristone is also used to facilitate difficult deliveries and to treat some hormone-dependent tumours, for example in breast cancer.

SEQUENCING THE HUMAN GENOME – 1988

Writing the book of genes

In 2001 an article in the journal *Nature* announced one of the most important events in the history of biology: the publication of the (almost) complete sequence of the human genome. The project had been born back in 1988 and over the ensuing 13 years involved some 2,000 researchers and cost $3 billion. Yet much still remained to be done. As the article concluded: 'The more we learn about the human genome, the more there is to explore.'

The article detailed the order in which the four nucleotide bases that constitute human DNA – known as A, T, G and C – are combined, together comprising all the genes making up our 23 pairs of chromosomes. This first draft, published in 2001, covered 90 per cent of the human genome – the complement of all our genes – with 99.9 per cent precision.

Getting involved

The project had got underway in the USA in 1988, when Congress decided to finance the research to sequence the human genome. The work was planned to last 16 years, with an annual budget of $200 million, and would be supervised by the Department of Energy and the National Institutes of Health, which set up a research centre under the direction of James Watson, co-discoverer (with Francis Crick) of the double-helix structure of DNA back in 1953.

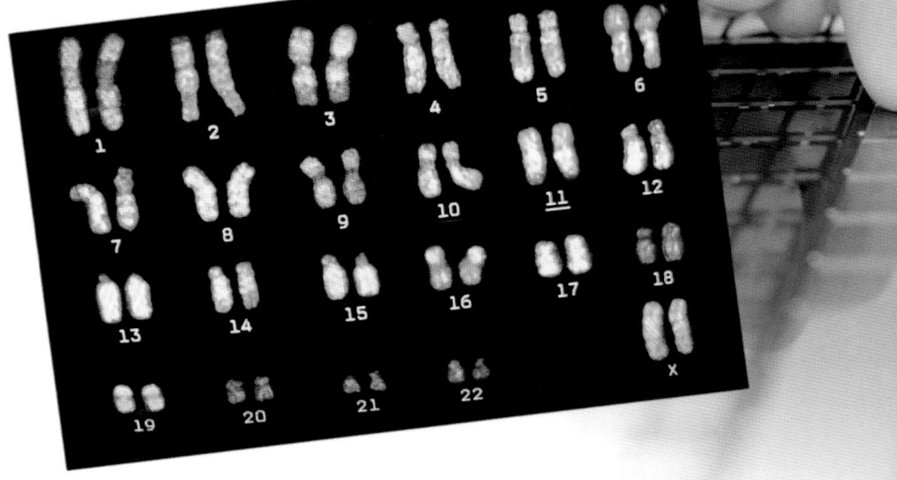

Two by two
The human karotype – the standard arrangement of chromosomes in a cell nucleus – comprises 46 chromosomes, arranged in 22 pairs of autosomes (which do not affect gender) and one pair of sex chromosomes, which do: women have two X chromosomes, men an X and a Y. This set (above) is that of a woman. Genetic inheritance can be seen in the facial resemblance of three generations of this family group (below). Which parts of her great-grandmother's 46 chromosomes might the youngest member have inherited?

The USA was not alone in its initiative. The Italians launched their own human genome programme in 1987, followed by the UK in 1989 and France in 1990.

New techniques were quickly put to use, improving access to the 3 billion bases that make up the human genome. The discovery of restriction enzymes in 1975 opened the way to genetic recombination, making it possible to replace, displace, add or suppress molecules of DNA. The use of yeast artificial chromosomes (YACs) and bacterial artificial chromosomes (BACs) enabled researchers to reproduce fragments of DNA thousands of pairs of bases long, as well as to make many replicas.

Deciphering the code
A researcher with a DNA microarray (above). These biotechnology tools enable scientists to analyse the state of gene expression (the active use of genetic information) at a given time and in a predetermined state in relation to a reference sample.

THE FIRST GENETIC MAP

The first genetic map of human chromosomes was published in 1992 by Jean Weissenbach, a biologist working at the Institute Pasteur. He and a colleague, Daniel Cohen, became involved in Généthon, a research institute set up by the French Association against Myopathies, taking an active part in the task of sequencing the human genome. Weissenbach developed a method of speeding up DNA analysis by using small repeating sequences known as microsatellites as molecular markers. He managed to identify more than 700 markers on the 23 separate pairs of chromosomes. When the map was completed three years later, 5,000 markers had been localised. The maps have been widely used, serving as references for the correct identification of hundreds of genes, including those responsible for a number of maladies.

FROM SMALL BEGINNINGS

Ahead of the sequencing of the human genome, the codes for simpler creatures were investigated and the techniques used as a model for tackling this enormous challenge. At the Sanger Centre in Cambridge (named after the Nobel prize-winning biochemist Fred Sanger and now known as the Wellcome Trust Sanger Institute), the genome of a yeast, *Saccharomyces cerevisiae,* with 12 million bases was the first to be completed in 1996. This was followed by the nematode worm, *Caenorhabditis elegans,* with 100 million bases in 1998. By the end of 1997, some 36 million bases of human DNA were being sequenced each year. By 1999 that figure had increased to 900 million a year.

These copies are indispensable for handling smaller fragments, both for determining the sequence of the bases that make them up and for reconstituting the entire chain. The development of the polymerase chain reaction technique in 1985 and the arrival of automated DNA sequencers two years later also did much to speed up the operation.

An international effort

This international effervescence represented not just a growing appreciation of the huge public-health benefits that could emerge from genetic research, but also of the potential economic benefits of sequencing human DNA, a vital first step in decrypting genes to allow genetic conditions to be identified and treated. Officially launched in 1990, the Human Genome Project was an international consortium. Financed by member states and by charitable organisations, it brought together more than 2,000 researchers in 20 different centres in half a dozen countries – China, France, Germany, Britain, Japan and the USA.

The programme had four objectives: to map the human genome; to establish the complete DNA sequence of humans and other model organisms; to develop ways of storing and analysing the information collected; and to promote other necessary technologies. Its supple management structures were founded on constant co-operation between the different laboratories involved in the quest.

Public or private?

Every year representatives from the various research centres met in Bermuda to compare notes. In 1996 they agreed the Bermuda

Principles, ensuring public access to the data by insisting that each new sequence be published within 24 hours of its discovery on one of three databases in the public domain. There was an urgent need for this measure, for private interests were by now making their presence felt. In 1990 the US biologist Craig Ventner had chosen a different research strategy, relying heavily on bioinformatics – the application of computer science to molecular biology. Impressed with the results, in 1998 he set up a private company, Celera Genomics, with the aim of commercialising the fruits of his researches. In face of this commerical

Genetic messenger
A transcription factor – seen here (right) as the mauve spiral in the process of binding to a DNA molecule – is a protein needed to control transcription, the process by which coding DNA is copied onto single-stranded RNA, which then carries the information around the cell.

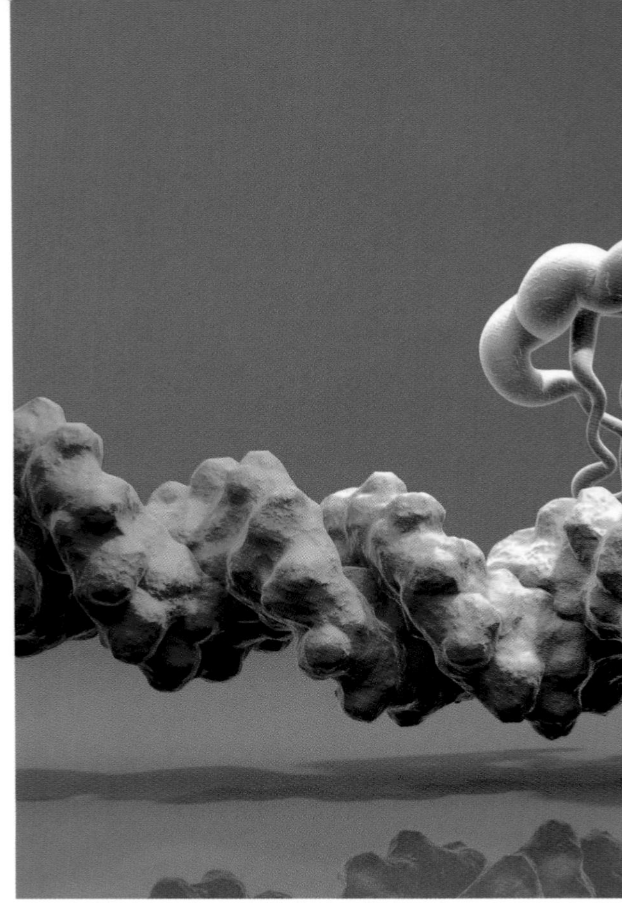

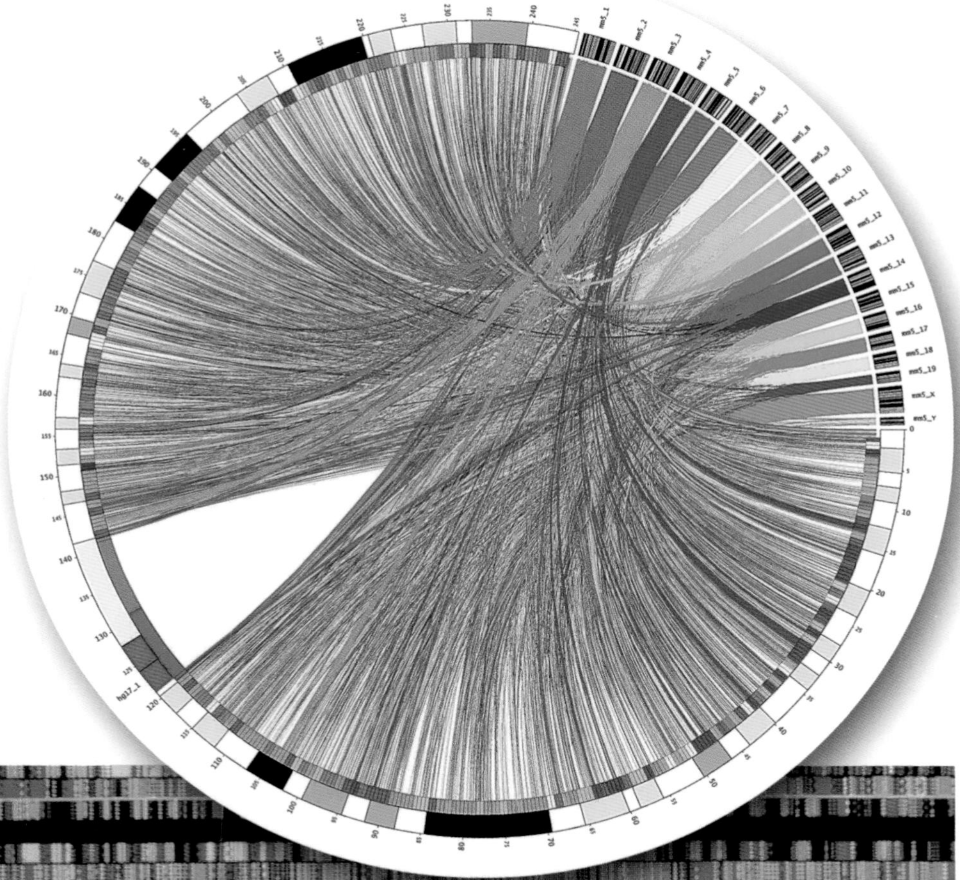

PATENTING GENES

The Celera Genomics affair pointed to the risks involved in privatising gene sequencing. In theory it is no longer possible to take out a patent on an individual gene or a gene sequence. What can be patented is any new application derived from knowledge of a gene, if it is considered both genuinely innovative and useful. But the terms of the law are so general that they allow room for widely differing interpretations, as in the ongoing lawsuit concerning diagnostic tests for breast cancer devised by the US-based firm Myriad Genetics. According to US government sources, 20 per cent of human genes are already affected in one way or another by existing patents.

Coloured strands and speckled bands
Genetic maps like this one (above left) indicate the relative positions of loci (the specific positions of genes or DNA markers) on a chromosome. The circular diagram shows the genetic material that is common to a mouse (represented on the outer rim of the top right quadrant) and to the human Chromosome 1 (the other three quadrants). The coloured lines link similar genes. Seen on a computer screen (left), human genome sequences appear in the form of a series of brightly coloured bands, with each colour – red, yellow, green or blue – representing one of the four nucleotide bases, A, T, G or C.

UNFINISHED BOOK

The gene map is a long way from resembling a straightforward operating manual. Genetic recombination, in which molecules of DNA break off and rejoin a chromosome at a different location, means that an individual's DNA can change over a lifetime. One of the most disconcerting examples is that of sufferers from a rare chromosomal disorder, XX male syndrome, who are genetically female but physiologically male. Then there are transposons, 'jumping' DNA sequences that can pass from one chromosome to another and form new genes. Finally, very little is known about so-called 'selfish DNA' – sequences that apparently reproduce for their own benefit rather than for that of the organism as a whole, which between them account for some 90 per cent of the entire genome.

threat, the international consortium decided in late 1998 to bring forward its own schedule by more than a year and complete the sequencing of the human genome by 2003. They also proposed to publish a draft covering 90 per cent of the genome by 2001. These new deadlines meant speeding up the sequencing process by a factor of 10.

The consortium published its first complete sequence, of Chromosome 22, in December 1999. Five months later Chromosome 21 followed. The draft was published in *Nature* in February 2001. Craig Ventner published his findings shortly after in the journal *Science*. He would later admit to having used some of the consortium's publicly disclosed results in his work. By 2006 the complete sequences of a dozen chromosomes had been published.

Still a long way to go

Once the gigantic task of sequencing was completed, all the letters of the book of life were spelled out in the correct order, but most of the words and phrases remained incomprehensible. Conservative estimates suggest that genes, which are most often scattered along the length of the DNA sequences, make up less than 10 per cent of the total, separated as they are by long stretches of non-coding material. And only a tiny percentage of the genes themselves have been identified. The function of half of them remains completely unknown.

Yet many genes implicated in human illnesses have been identified and located. When just a single abnormal gene is involved, as in the case of various muscular conditions, it is possible to envisage a genetic therapy that could replace it. Improved knowledge of certain genes also enables doctors to propose new treatments better fitted to their patients' needs. Much more research will be required to understand fully the innermost functioning of the human organism. Dozens of different genes are involved in the mechanisms responsible for the majority of conditions, many of them still unidentified. A full understanding of the human genome is still decades away.

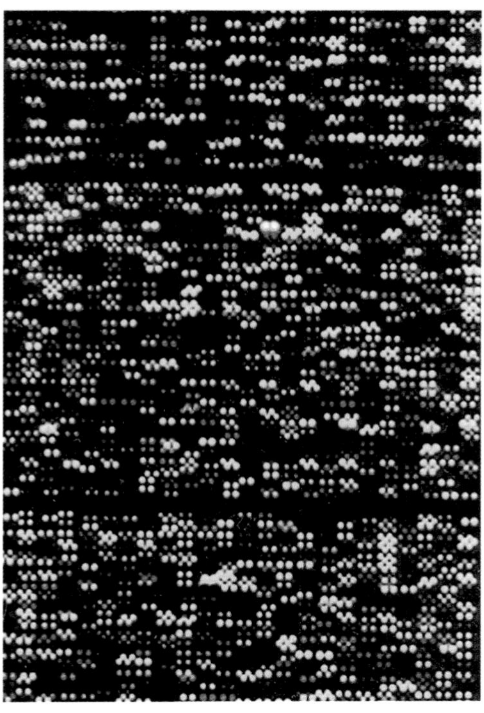

Know your enemy
This microarray (right) shows the genome of Bacillus subtilis, *a micro-organism considered an excellent model for the study of pathogenic bacteria like* Streptococcus pneumoniae *and for finding ways of combating them.*

MARSHALL McLUHAN – 1911 TO 1980

Understanding new media and the global village

Canada's Marshall McLuhan had barely completed his engineering studies when he decided to devote himself instead to modern literature. But no sooner was he committed to the humanities than his attention started swinging to technology. Turning his back on his 1943 thesis on symbolism and his subsequent researches into the Elizabethan poets, he found his way to the Center for Culture and Technology in Toronto, becoming its director. In the early 1960s, he turned his spotlight on communications and the media, a field in which he quickly gained an international reputation.

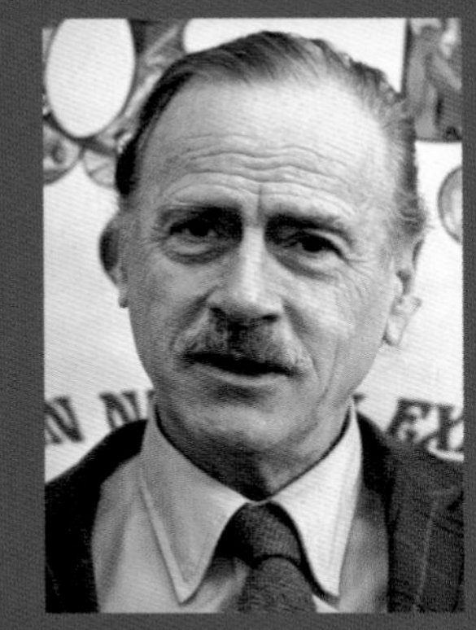

More than a few people were irritated by Marshall McLuhan's wide range of interests and his highly unacademic way of addressing them. He seemed to take a positive delight in trampling on the toes of traditionalists who believed that the development and exchange of ideas could only function smoothly if historians stuck to history, philosophers to philosophy and sociologists to sociology.

From one galaxy to another

In 1962 McLuhan published *The Gutenberg Galaxy*, a seminal work putting his own spin on the march of humanity. He described three eras of human communications, starting with the primitive stage without writing, when the exchange of news relied exclusively on the spoken word. Then came the revolution brought about by the spread of printing, which multiplied the sources of information and in time vastly encouraged the spread of mass literacy. Finally, McLuhan saw the citizens of his own day as inhabiting the 'Marconi Galaxy' at the dawn of a fresh, electronic era. In this new age the messages conveyed by the media became simpler, no longer addressing a single reader but rather aimed at everyone: the entire human family found itself gathered 'into a single global tribe'.

McLuhan's own message was not always easy to understand. On the cover of one foreign edition, the publisher praised the 'prodigiously wide culture' of the author, but felt obliged to warn readers not to expect 'a logical line of thought expressed in solidly constructed chapters, but rather a succession of points of view, of illuminations and flashes sparked by bringing together the most wildly disparate texts'.

In the 1970s McLuhan established his reputation as critic-in-chief of the new world of mass communications, denouncing the influence of the all-powerful media, which he viewed as capable of shaping people's personalities and behaviour. In his view, the big issue confronting society had a Biblical simplicity: people had either to control the media or else be controlled by them.

24-hour news
Today it is almost impossible to escape news information carried by a multiplicity of channels to even the most remote parts of the world.

Global village
A citizen of Kanak in France's Pacific dependency of New Caledonia watches a politician in Paris commenting on the violent stand-off that set local independence fighters against the French authorities in 1988.

The medium is the message

McLuhan's warning was still in people's minds when *The Global Village* was published posthumously in 1988 (he had died in 1980). Why give a new, universal dimension to that most humble of human communities? As always, McLuhan was provocative, bringing together disparate ideas. The electronic era, he believed, was creating a planet on which everyone lived at the same rhythm and in the same space, nurtured by instantaneous information. The communication networks linking the planet had become an extension of people's own cognitive systems. The content of the information fed in moment by moment was less important for McLuhan than the channels that carried it: 'the medium is the message'.

Although McLuhan died too soon to devote much attention to the digital revolution, the coming of the Internet quickly proved the relevance of his analysis. Many of the disciples who subsequently took up his mantle were quick to spell out the dangers that the new media posed: a blanket of conformity risked cloaking all communication, extinguishing the last vestiges of spontaneity. The same news available everywhere at the same time; windows on people's private lives flung open on sites like Facebook; elliptical phrases transmitted at the speed of light via text messaging or Twitter – all of these developments indicate that an unprecedented cultural revolution is underway. McLuhan can justly claim to have been its prophet.

Any time, anywhere
A man reading an electronic newspaper carried on the Internet (below left).

A LONG-HELD CONCERN

Are we right to be worried about the possible excesses of the electronic communications era, prefigured by Marshall McLuhan, and the damage it risks to our minds and capacity for independent thought? Anyone thinking along such lines might do well to look back at the concerns expressed by Socrates in Plato's dialogue *Phaedrus*, written in the 4th century BC. According to Plato, Socrates worried that the spread of the written word, a radical innovation, risked robbing people of their memories, kept in good repair by the constant need to express themselves through speech. While the young Phaedrus extolled the reading of papyrus manuscripts, Socrates wondered whether the practice might not hinder the development of good judgment, best formed through spoken dialogue between two interlocutors. Times and context may change, it seems, but some concerns never go away.

THE INTERNET – 1989

A connected world

The arrival of the World Wide Web brought the Internet to the public at large. Within just a few years this sophisticated tool, created by and for scientists, would transform our way of living, working and doing business.

Father of the Web
Tim Berners-Lee (above right) used this NeXT computer (above) to develop – in collaboration with Robert Cailliau – the concept of hypertexts that underlies the creation of the World Wide Web.

The Internet as we now know it took off in 1989. In that year NSFNet, the principal access point to what specialists were already calling 'an' internet, opened its doors to commercial traffic, meaning that this network of networks was no longer exclusively reserved for use by universities. By coincidence, 1989 was also the year when Tim Berners-Lee invented what would become the World Wide Web. For the Internet and the Web are not the same thing. To understand the difference, it is necessary to go a little further back in time.

The network's origins

In 1957 scientists in the USSR launched Sputnik 1, the first artificial satellite. The US government responded the following February by creating, under the aegis of the Department of Defense, the Advanced Research Projects Agency (ARPA) as a first step towards regaining the lead in technological progress. The ARPA's task was to promote futuristic research, and its scientists were encouraged to give their imaginations free rein. Between them, they came up with the idea of putting computers in communication with one another, rather than simply using them as calculating machines. In August 1962 the US computer scientist Joseph Carl Licklider published his vision of a universal network of computers that would enable their users to make contact with each other wherever they happened to be. Two months later he was in charge of ARPA's information research programme.

In the same year Leonard Kleinrock of the Massachusetts Institute of Technology (MIT) formulated the first theory of packet communication. This involved fragmenting messages into data packets, each provided with a label and a destination address, that travelled independently over the telephone network to be reassembled when they reached their destination. There was no need for a special circuit to carry the messages as they simply became part of the general traffic on the line – unlike telephone conversations, for example, which required a line to themselves.

In 1967 ARPA unveiled the Arpanet project, linking a chain of university computers to its own network. Two years later the first packet switch – the name given to computers serving as marshalling yards for information, nowadays known as routers – was installed on the University of California Los Angeles (UCLA) campus, linking a UCLA science-department computer to one at the Stanford Research Institute some 300 miles to the north. This marked the first time that computers exchanged data. Arpanet expanded rapidly.

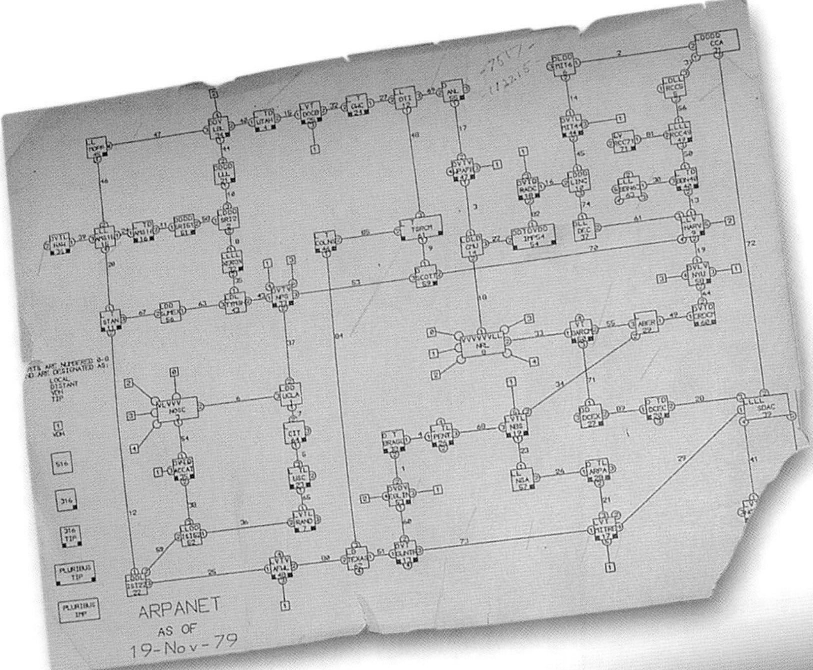

Small beginnings
A diagram of the Arpanet network (left) as it looked in November 1979. The grid expanded rapidly, eventually linking almost 4 million separate hubs and more than a thousand computers around the globe.

Mapping Internet use
An illustration of the flow of data on NSFNet in the USA in September 1991 (below). The white lines at the top represent the links between the supercomputers that made up the nation's Internet infrastructure. The vertical lines show how data was redistributed from these supercomputers to regional centres.

At the same time other US universities were setting up internal networks to exchange data files. In 1972 American computer programmer Ray Tomlinson developed the first electronic mail software, and e-mails soon took up a major part of network traffic. Since there was no question of wasting bandwidth for anything other than academic research, parallel networks were created for other purposes. One of these was Usenet, founded by students in 1979 to host newsgroups devoted to special-interest subjects from chess to science fiction.

The true birth of the Internet

By now, the idea of connecting all the various grids into a network of networks was starting to take shape. Plans to link Arpanet to CSNet (CS stood for 'Computer Science'), a similar programme linking a separate group of universities, got under way in 1980 and the connection was made three years later. The first true Internet – the word itself had been used as early as 1972 – could be said to be this one joining CSNet to the university section of Arpanet (the military in effect chose to shut off their part of the network, which thereafter had a separate identity as Milnet).

In 1985 NSFNet (the National Science Foundation Net) was established, connecting five supercomputers in different US universities by high-speed lines. NSFNet soon came to serve as the backbone of the system, linking the Arpanet/CSNet nexus to a variety of local grids. The Internet became a global phenomenon linking all US universities with their Canadian and European counterparts.

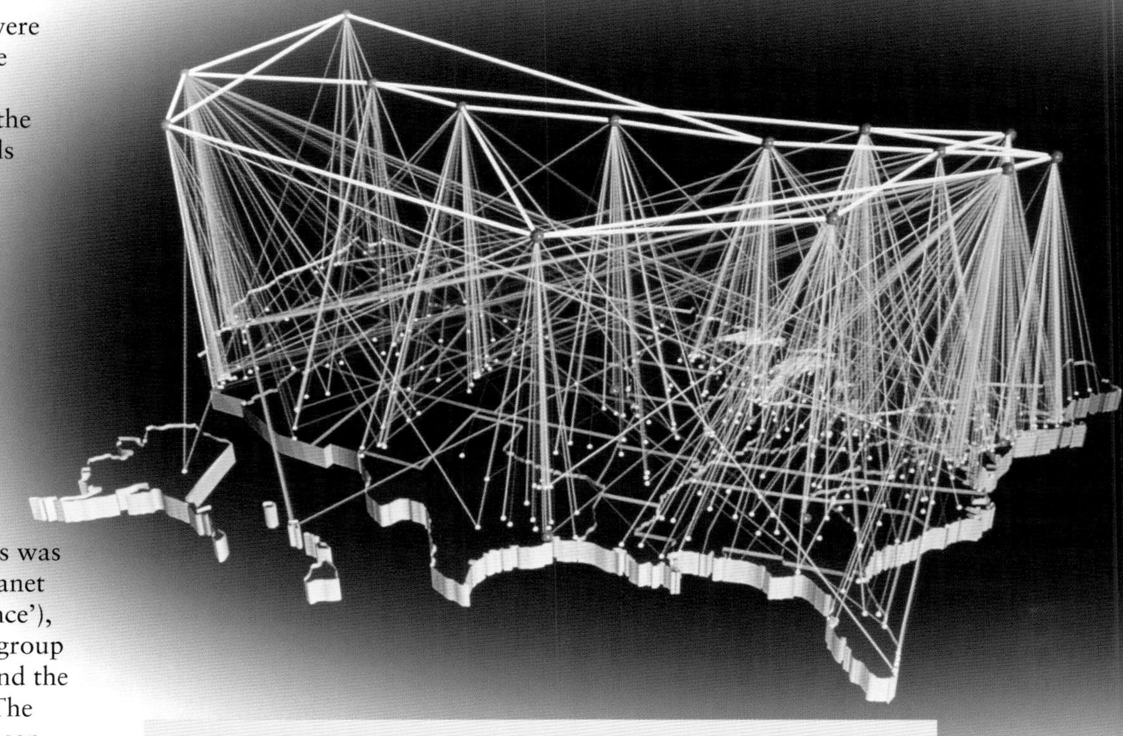

MANAGING THE WEB

In 1992 a group of Internet pioneers founded the Internet Society (ISOC), giving it a worldwide remit. At a time when Internet use was expanding fast, they felt the need for a body that could help to coordinate the development of networks around the globe. At the heart of the Society is the Internet Engineering Task Force (IETF), an informal group open to all engineers and researchers, whose job is to develop the Internet standards that ISOC promotes. The Public Interest Registry supervises '.org' sites. The Internet Corporation for Assigned Names and Numbers (ICANN), a not-for-profit California-based organisation also exercising worldwide authority, was set up in 1998 to allocate addresses and manage domains and name formats.

The engine room
The data centre, a specialised facility for data-processing equipment, is the backbone of any network. Equipment is usually stored in racks in single file, as here (below).

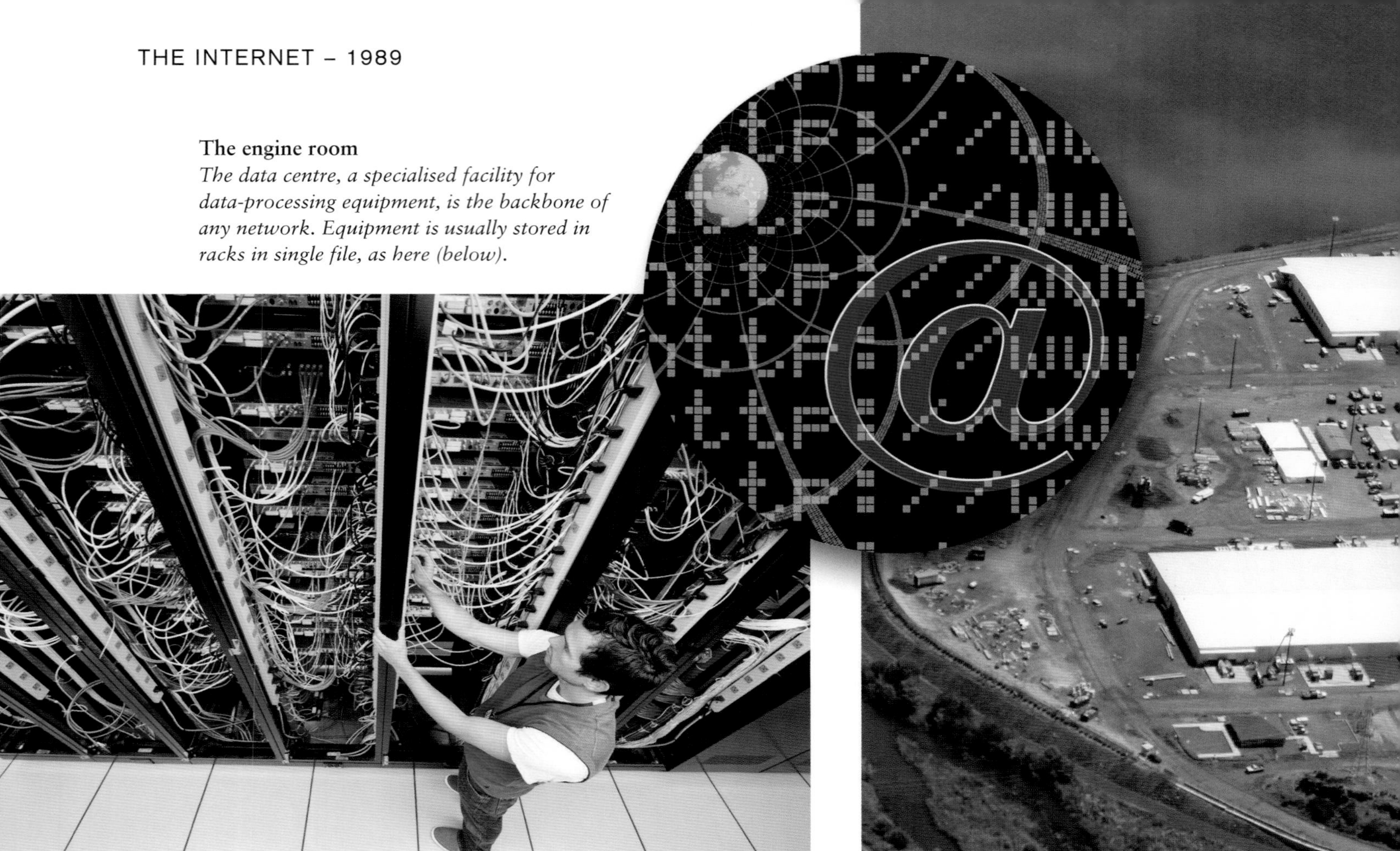

The coming of the Web

On 13 March, 1989, at the European Organisation for Nuclear Research (usually known from its French acronym as CERN) in Geneva, the London-born physicist Tim Berners-Lee proposed a totally new virtual architecture that would share the data on the organisation's internal network more efficiently. The proposal was based on the concept of hypertext. In each document, some information units (usually specific words) would serve as anchors. By connecting all the anchors with hyperlinks, it would be possible to pass automatically from one to another and so access all the documents containing them.

Working with the Belgian engineer Robert Cailliau, Berners-Lee went on to develop the concept into what would become known as the World Wide Web. Between them, they invented the three fundamental elements of any hypertext system: a mark-up language, which they called HTML (HyperText Mark-up Language), to format pages and to include the hyperlinks (more accurately, the anchors); a protocol governing the transfer of information between the server and the user, known as http (HyperText Transfer Protocol); and 'addresses' identifying each of the pages downloaded and indicating the way in which they could be accessed – that is, the language involved and the protocol transfer used. This is what makes it possible to make the connection when an Internet user clicks on a hypertext link.

In 1991 Tim Berners-Lee publicly announced the Internet's existence on Usenet. Stanford University's particle accelerator research team immediately opened a Web server, linked to that of CERN. Two years later CERN put the Web software in the public domain and the World Wide Web was born.

Keys to the Internet
The @ symbol separates usernames from hostnames in email addresses; http is the protocol governing transfer of information between servers and users; www stands for World Wide Web.

INTERNET SERVICE PROVIDERS

In 1994 NSFNet, having lost its role as the Internet's gateway, designed a new architecture for the grid based on network access points. Four private firms signed contracts and a new profession was born: that of Internet service provider. An ISP operator needs a large computer (the router), plenty of high-bit-rate connections, and as many contracts for data exchange with other networks as possible. The ISP then becomes a hub of the wider network, with the job of managing the flow of data. Some firms have gone on to offer their services to thousands of private subscribers, becoming access providers. Most also sell additional services to their clients, including mailboxes, web hosting, access to Usenet and so forth. Today, ISPs also offer hook-ups to telephone services and television channels.

ALL FOR FREE?

The huge mine of information that is now available to everyone often gives users the impression that the Internet is – or should be – free. In fact this is rarely the case, since sites offering free services are mostly supported by advertising revenues. Peer-to-peer file sharing enables individuals to share music or films over the network, but even if no money exchanges hands, the fact of publishing works on the web without remunerating the artists or companies constitutes copyright piracy, and the film and music industries are doing their utmost to stop the practice.

Google home
The Dalles, Oregon, was once known as the end of the Oregon trail. Today, this small town of some 12,000 inhabitants is home to two gigantic data centres, each the size of a football field, built by the Internet company Google.

The Web is a system of hypertext documents, operating in the public domain via the Internet, which links pages put online on server sites that are accessed via web-browser software. If computer users do not know the address of sites that might interest them, they can connect up to a search engine such as Google, which will almost instantly locate the addresses of any and all pages containing material relevant to the subject.

The first World Wide Web Conference was held in May 1994. Later that year Berners-Lee set up the World Wide Web Consortium (W3C) to develop operating standards for the network. In the ensuing years the number of sites and web pages grew exponentially. Today there are more than 200 million servers, putting billions of information pages online. In addition, there may be up to 100 times as many documents not accessible to the public.

Exotic bloom
Although it may look like coral (right), this image is in fact a computer graphic showing Internet traffic between servers in four different countries. The pink areas represent the USA, dark blue the UK, light blue Italy and light green Sweden.

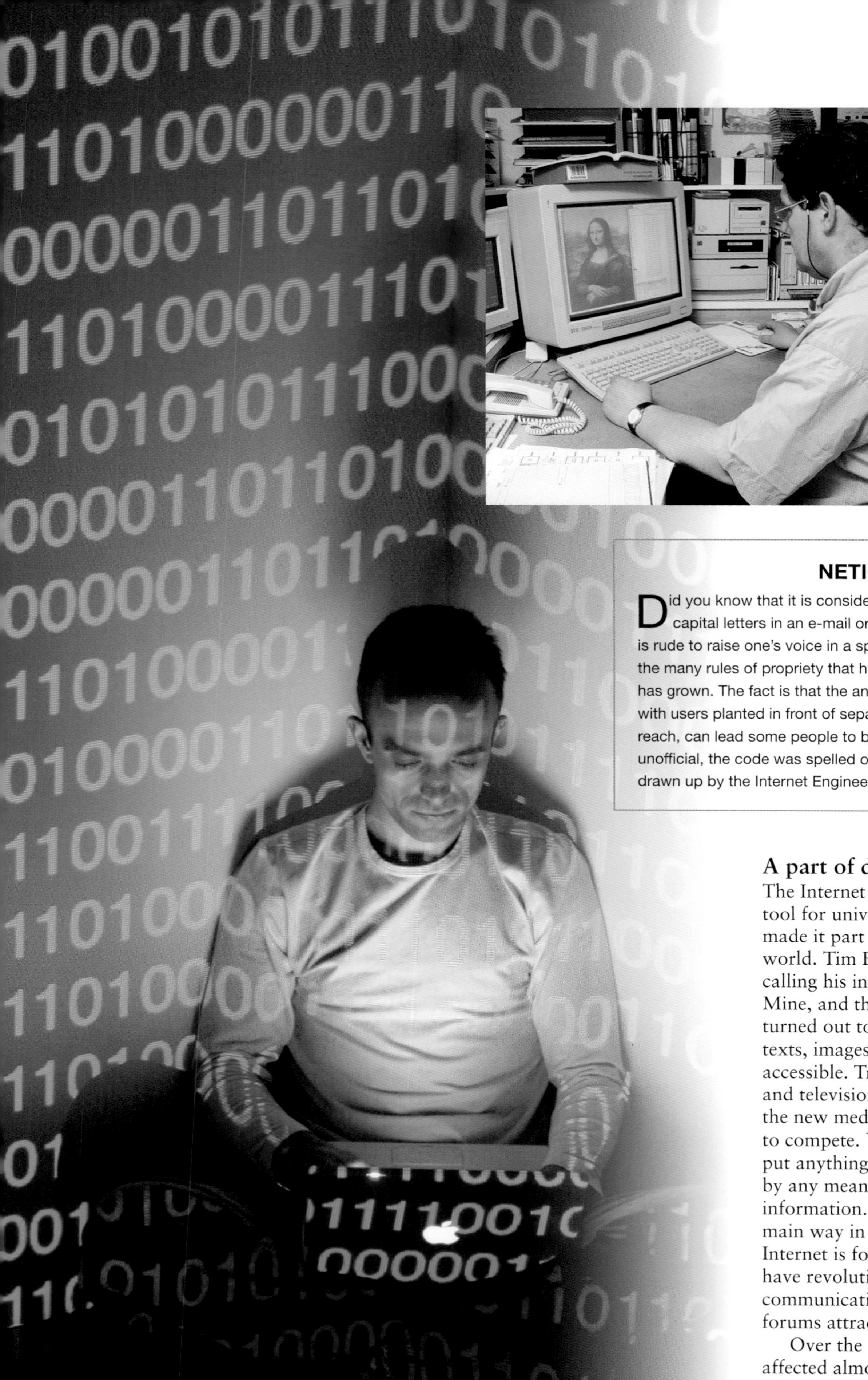

Going online
Enthusiastic computer-users were once referred to generically as 'hackers', but that word now suggests individuals using their expertise to break through security systems. Whatever the purpose, going online is energy-intensive: one click on Google uses as much electricity as a light bulb consumes in an hour.

NETIQUETTE

Did you know that it is considered bad behaviour to put words in capital letters in an e-mail or an online discussion group, just as it is rude to raise one's voice in a spoken conversation? This is just one of the many rules of propriety that have become accepted as the Internet has grown. The fact is that the anonymity of Internet communication, with users planted in front of separate screens well out of one another's reach, can lead some people to behave unacceptably. At first purely unofficial, the code was spelled out in 1995 in the form of a memo drawn up by the Internet Engineering Task Force.

A part of daily life

The Internet may have started life as a working tool for universities, but the arrival of the Web made it part of daily life for people all over the world. Tim Berners-Lee at one time considered calling his invention TIM, The Information Mine, and that is precisely what the Web has turned out to be, bringing together a mass of texts, images and sounds, all of them instantly accessible. Traditional media like newspapers and television channels have had to adapt to the new medium, and some have found it hard to compete. Yet because almost anyone can put anything they like on line, the Web is not by any means always a reliable source of information. Alongside Web surfing, the other main way in which the public at large use the Internet is for e-mails and blogging, which have revolutionised both public and private communications. On-line gaming and specialist forums attract a more limited clientele.

Over the past two decades, the Internet has affected almost every aspect of social life. Millions of people buy goods online every day, spend their leisure time there and use the Net to seek partners or broadcast details of their own

You've Got Mail
In Nora Ephron's 1998 romcom, Tom Hanks and Meg Ryan play two individuals who meet over the Internet and form a perfectly matched virtual couple, but in real life plenty of things conspire to keep them apart.

private lives. People turn to the Web for information, to book travel tickets, to access their bank accounts and to buy and sell stocks and shares. Many even work online.

In just a few years, the Internet has become indispensable to the modern world. People even speak of a 'digital divide' separating those who have access to it from those who have not, whether in the developed and developing worlds or between succeeding generations of a given society.

Ever-expanding possibilities

In about 2004, Web 2.0 was born and the Web is still continuing to evolve, becoming steadily more interactive. Users are no longer content merely to visit sites but are increasingly seeking to participate in them. New uses constantly show up, such as on-line chat rooms which were introduced in 1996 on ICQ, an instant-messaging programme developed by the Israeli company Mirabilis, before being taken up by, among others, Yahoo Messenger in 1998 and MSN Messenger a year later. Blogs, a sort of private diary made public online, have become part of our way of life, while sites such as Facebook, Myspace and Twitter have created virtual social networks.

In 2008 the Internet played a significant part in the US presidential elections, when an unprecedented grassroots campaign enabled the Democratic Party challenger Barack Obama to build up a financial war-chest that far exceeded those of his rivals and to win his party's nomination. Learning the lesson of his success, all political candidates in democratic countries now have their own websites.

In economic terms, the Internet has become a vast marketplace, with the volume of online trading transactions never ceasing to grow (although many traditional businesses have found it hard to find their place within it). It has a cosmopolitan character, crossing frontiers and borders: a student in Argentina can use it to converse in real time with a German professor, while an Italian writer can exchange views with a Tibetan monk … And the Internet has become the preferred medium for minority or dissident communities seeking a channel by which they can freely exchange information and opinions.

Global connections
A crowded Internet café (below) in Ho Chi Minh City, Vietnam. The Internet has spread all round the world, with only Africa still under-represented.

ABUSING THE INTERNET

Any tool as powerful and universal as the Internet could hardly hope to escape some degree of misuse. A majority of the e-mails downloaded today are unasked for and unwanted. Spam mail generally takes the form of messages soliciting business, sent automatically to millions of individuals who never asked to receive them. Worse still is phishing, which involves dispatching e-mails sporting fake bank logos or similar devices in the hope of extracting account details from the recipients. As for hacking, it exploits weaknesses in computer security systems to access privileged information.

The Internet

Like all inventions, the Internet did not come out of nothing. Rather, it was the end product of earlier breakthroughs, including the telephone and computer. More than a cable network on a global scale, it is a complex system bringing together computers, software and futuristic ideas in concrete form.

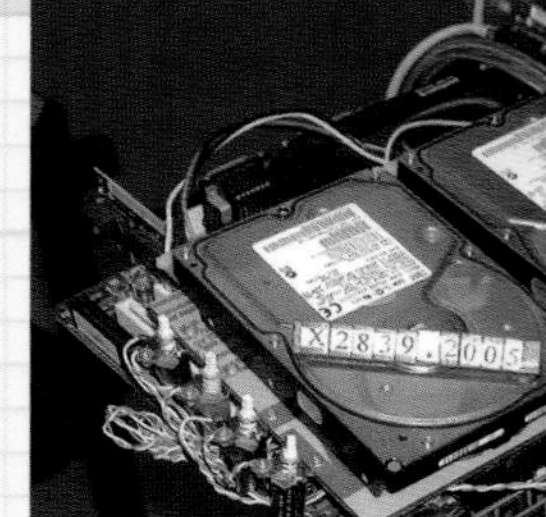

Above: Inside a Google web server

Above left: An example of html (HyperText Mark-up Language)

COMMUNICATION PROTOCOLS
FROM NCP TO HTTP

For packets of information to be transferred from one computer to another, the two must speak the same language and recognise e-mail addresses. The rules governing such communication are collectively known as a protocol. Arpanet used the Network Control Protocol (NCP), originally laid out in 1970, but this soon proved not to be up to the task and so a replacement, the TCP/IP (Transmission Control Protocol/Internet Protocol), was developed to replace it. The US Ministry of Defense tried out TCP/IP from 1976 on and persuaded Arpanet to switch over to the new code in January 1983. On the World Wide Web, hypertext pages use a special protocol – http (Hypertext Transfer Protocol).

HYPERTEXT
FROM MEMEX TO THE WEB

In 1945 a US engineer, Vannevar Bush, came up with the idea of a sort of electronic office he called the memex. This theoretical machine was to be linked to a library of microfilms that it could track down on demand via an index. The concept already contained the seeds of hypertext links, providing access to documents via key words. In 1965 Ted Nelson introduced the notion of hypermedia, using other means than text alone to communicate information. In 1987 Apple launched the basic software for HyperCard, the first commercial hypermedia operation, and two years later Tim Berners-Lee created the Web, a global hypertext system operated over the Internet.

INTERNET TOOLS
FROM E-MAILS TO THE TELEPHONE

The first e-mail software, produced in 1972 for use on Arpanet, already had the @ symbol present in it. As the Web grew, portals and hosting sites found themselves having to cope with a steadily increasing flow of messages. In 1990 Tim Berners-Lee created Nexus, the first browser linking users to specific web pages. Microsoft introduced Internet Explorer in 1995, ten years before Mozilla Firefox came into service as a free alternative. Also in 1995, a group of Stanford University students created Yahoo!, a search engine using key words to locate sites. Google was founded three years later, and quickly became the most widely used data miner. By then images were circulating widely on the Net, the first webcam having come into use in 1991. Voice transmission over the Internet using IP (Internet Protocol) dates from 1996, paving the way for Skype's introduction of Internet telephone services in 2003.

Above: The @ sign, a logo for electronic mail

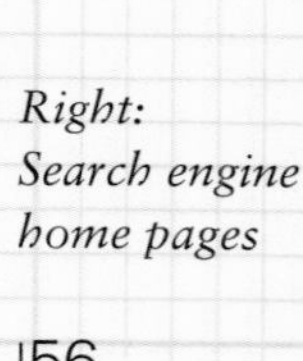

Right: Search engine home pages

WEB SERVERS

BIGGER AND BIGGER

The very first Web server was Tim Berners-Lee's microcomputer. As the number of subscribers and the amount of traffic have grown, the main sites have had to avail themselves of ever more powerful equipment. Today, Google employs almost 2 million computers, housed in parks covering many acres. Internet demand is now so great that electricity consumption is beginning to cause problems for the servers, as is the need to prevent hardware from overheating.

ACCESS AND EXIT PORTALS

FROM BELL MODEMS TO THE DSL

Telephone lines transmit an electric current in the form of an analogue signal, but computers can only understand digital languages. It thus became necessary to invent devices capable of transforming analogue data into a digital format, and vice versa. These are the so-called modulators-demodulators, better known as modems. The first on the market was developed by Bell Laboratories in 1958. The earliest models used standard telephone lines, taking up all the available bandwidth. DSL (Digital Subscriber Line) modems – ADSL is the best-known – have been introduced since; these code the data digitally on frequencies higher than those used for human voices, leaving the rest of the line free to carry telephone conversations. Modems linked to cable television networks make use of radio frequencies.

Connecting cables

Web-server wiring

CONNECTING UP

FROM COPPER WIRE TO FIBRE OPTICS

In its early days the Internet made use of the twisted copper wires of the public telephone network, employing Integrated Service Digital Network (ISDN) communication standards that offered a bandwidth of at best 2 Mbit/sec. Since 2000, Digital Subscriber Line (DSL) technology has made it possible to increase that figure by a factor of 10. Television coaxial cables also offer several dozen megabits per second. Optical fibres have gradually come to replace copper wire, whether for telephone or television delivery. By the time it reaches the consumer, bandwidth can now stretch to several gigabits a second.

Computer connected to the Internet

THE FUTURE OF THE INTERNET

MOBILE AND SEMANTIC

Whether in the form of computers, laptops or games consoles, Internet hardware is getting steadily smaller. The future lies with smartphones, the most advanced form of mobiles, which will enable tomorrow's users to access the Net from any point on the globe. Meanwhile, servers will follow the evolution of computers, becoming ever more powerful, although the present semi-conductor technology is reaching its limits and may well give way to some new model in tomorrow's computers. The future may lie with optical or quantum computers; no-one knows for sure. The Web will be revolutionised by the coming of search engines capable not just of seeking out elementary units of information but also of interpreting the user's intention in entering a request. This 'semantic Web' will open the way for much more sophisticated searches than are possible today.

Third-generation personal digital assistant (PDA)

Self-adhesive stamps 1988

The very first self-adhesive stamps were introduced in Sierra Leone and Tonga in 1964 as a response to the prevailing humidity, which in a tropical climate tended to liquefy the gum on traditional stamps. The first developed country to take up the idea was Canada, in 1988, and the USA and Japan followed suit the year after. Britain's Royal Mail did not produce the new stamps until January 2001, following market research that showed that 93 per cent of testers preferred them; they were also reckoned to take up to 12 per cent less time when preparing an envelope for posting. The original Royal Mail issue featured bright orange stamps for first-class and blue for second-class, both still bearing the image of the Queen's head, soon to be required by law.

Peel and stick
A strip of US stamps patriotically displays the Stars and Stripes and the Statue of Liberty. Today, more than 90 per cent of stamps issued around the world are self-adhesive.

Electronic tagging 1989

Keeping tabs
Almost 2,000 young offenders were tagged in the UK in 2009, more than half of whom were subsequently reported to have either removed the tag or broken their terms of curfew.

The first trial of electronic tagging took place with psychiatric patients in Massachusetts in 1967, but it was the 1980s before it was seriously considered as an alternative to prison sentences for criminals. In 1989 experiments began in Britain with electronic tagging as part of bail conditions, and subsequently this way of keeping track of individuals has been put to use with convicted offenders subject to curfew, prisoners on parole and, in the case of control orders under the Prevention of Terrorism Act, people thought likely to be planning an offence. Intended to relieve the pressure on prisons and ease the transfer of inmates back into society, the devices are usually worn around the ankle and transmit signals to a receiver in the offender's home. This 'base station' is attached to a telephone line, allowing the supervising authorities to check that the tagged individual is where he or she is meant to be; if not, an alarm is sounded. The idea was originally promoted in England by Tom Stacey, journalist and penologist. In 2010 the cost of tagging was estimated to be £675 a month, compared with £1,555 for keeping an offender in prison.

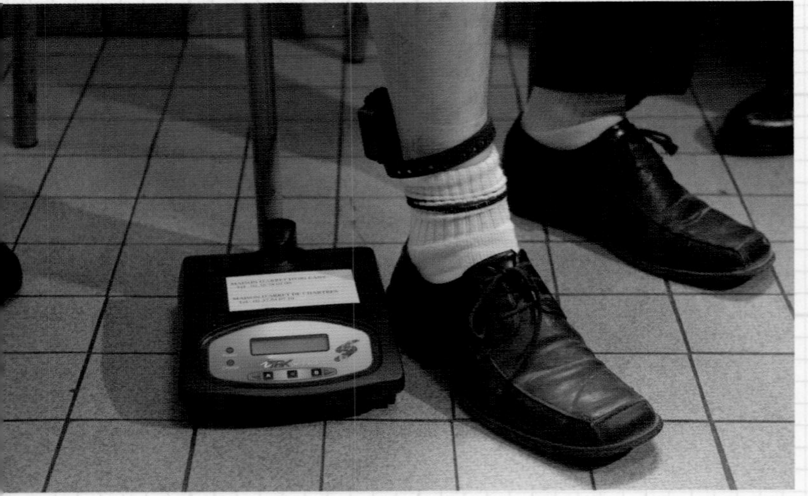

SHOCK BRACELETS

In 2009 a Canadian firm, Lamperd Less Lethal, proposed an ID device designed to improve air security. Intended for use by all airline passengers, it took the form of a bracelet fitted with RFID (Radio Frequency Identification) that could be used to track the wearer both in the airport and during the flight. Anyone exhibiting suspect behaviour could be immobilised by a stun device similar to a Taser, remotely controlled by a designated crew member.

Touchscreens 1989

One-touch solution
Researchers had dreamed of computers that would execute commands at a touch long before new technology finally made the idea possible.

In 1989 the US firm GRiD Systems marketed its GRiDPAD, a forerunner of the Palm Pilot personal digital assistant and the first portable minicomputer with a touchscreen and stylus. The technology involved was not, in fact, new. As far back as 1972, IBM had demonstrated the PLATO IV computer, equipped with a plasma screen that used an infrared system to register touch. Five years later, new resistive technology brought electronic sensors into play: placed at the four corners of the screen, these could locate and measure the pressure of a finger or a stylus. The first personal computer with a touchscreen was the HP-150, launched by Hewlett-Packard in 1983. Two years later a US company, Zenith Electronics, marketed the first touchscreen system based on surface acoustic wave technology, which involves analysing waves generated by touch and can respond to any solid object. Fresh, interactive applications are still being developed and introduced, such as at tourist information points, rail ticket machines and cash dispensers, while smartphones offer a whole range of possibilities.

GRAPHICS TABLETS

Since the start of the Information Age, manufacturers and commercial enterprises have felt a growing need to rapidly convert hand-written messages into electronic text and to turn hand-drawn sketches into computer graphics. Graphics tablets do just that. As far back as 1964 the Graphic Converter or RAND Grafacon used a grid of wires beneath the screen to facilitate both tasks. The touchscreens employed on newer devices are more adaptable and easier to use.

Biodegradable plastic 1989

Plastic waste has a life cycle of at least a century and can survive for up to a thousand years. To reduce the massive amount of environmental pollution caused, not least by some 12 billion plastic bags thrown away each year, a team of researchers at the Italian chemical firm Ferruzzi developed a partially biodegradable product in 1989. Composed of five parts cornstarch to four of oil-derived hydrocarbons or polymers and one of plasticisers, Mater-Bi® dissipates in three to eight weeks. Even so, the phthalates used as plasticisers remain non-biodegradable.

Dressed to kill
A man makes his protest against environmental pollution at a 2007 demonstration in San Francisco. Discarded plastic bags cause huge damage to marine and other wildlife.

GENE THERAPY – 1990

Using genes to treat diseases

On 14 September, 1990, a team led by William French Anderson and Michael Blaese of the US National Institutes of Health made medical history. They injected a four-year-old girl with her own white blood cells, which had previously been removed from her body and genetically modified. The young girl was suffering from a lethal immunodeficiency disorder and the goal was to correct the deficient gene responsible.

Genes are segments of DNA that the body's cells decode to produce proteins, in much the same way that someone reading a book makes sense of a phrase by deciphering a series of words made up of individual letters. If one of the four A, G, T and C bases, whose sequence forms genes, is switched for another in what is referred to as a mutation, the normal protein is either no longer produced or else cannot carry out its physiological functions.

The four-year-old girl about to make history suffered from adenosine deaminase deficiency, a form of severe combined immune deficiency (SCID) also known as 'Bubble Boy' Syndrome, so called because most of those affected are boys, some of whom can only survive by remaining in a totally sterile environment. Adenosine deaminase (ADA) is an enzyme, the absence of which had reduced the girl's immune defences to the point where she was forced to live in such a bubble. In her case the gene therapy involved removing some of her white blood cells, or lymphocytes. Using a vector in an appropriate culture, a corrected gene coding for the missing enzyme (a form of protein) was then introduced into her DNA in the cells – a process known as ex vivo therapy. The modified cells were then injected back into her bloodstream.

Seeing the unseeable
A digital image of a DNA molecule (above), compared with an actual image of a plasmid (right) obtained through a transmission electron microscope. Plasmids are DNA fragments that can live and reproduce independently of chromosomes. Nowadays they are used to modify the genetic material of organisms like bacteria.

Gene therapy, then, involves introducing genetic material into a person's organism. By 1990 adenosine deaminase deficiency was already being treated using a form of synthetic ADA delivered in a polyethylene glycol (PEG) vehicle. But the treatment regime was highly demanding, requiring an intramuscular injection once or twice a week for life – with no real guarantee that it would work. Another option was a bone marrow transplant, but for this the bone marrow had to come from a genetically compatible donor, preferably another member of the same family. Only gene therapy seemed to hold out the possibility of a genuine cure.

GENE VECTORS

In most cases modified viruses are used as the vectors of corrected genes. These viruses insert their own genetic material into the genome of cells they infect, but it is possible to neutralise this effect by introducing the corrected gene into the genome of the virus and deactivating the viral sequences responsible for their multiplication. The most common choices are either adenoviruses and others associated with them or else retroviruses, especially the lentiviruses (which include HIV in their ranks). Other vectors still in the experimental stage include liposomes, nanoparticles and lipid microspheres.

Bubble boy
In children suffering from 'Bubble Boy' Syndrome – the official title is Severe Combined Immune Deficiency Syndrome, or SCID – the immune system is either non-existent or very weak. This means that their bodies are not equipped to deal with infections. To survive, they must live in a completely sterile environment. Gene therapy to repair the deficient DNA cells holds out hope of finding an effective treatment for the condition.

Bringing in outside genes

The precursor of this method was transgenesis, first tried in 1971 by US biochemists Herbert Boyer, Stanley Cohen and Paul Berg, who pioneered recombinant DNA processes that involved the technique of gene splicing. In 1977 Boyer and his colleagues used transgenic bacteria to produce somatostatin, a human protein. Four years later the first transgenic mice were created. By then the genetic genie was well and truly out of the bottle.

The new era dawned through slow and painstaking advances in genetic science. Researchers were beginning to learn how to localise, detect and then identify genes on chromosomes. It still took years to identify a gene on a genetic map, using a method known as positional cloning, and then after that it took months to work out the DNA sequence involved, meaning the order of the letters composing it. Some conditions were relatively straightforward to track down, like Duchenne muscular dystrophy, identified in 1986. But it was only after the year 2000 and the

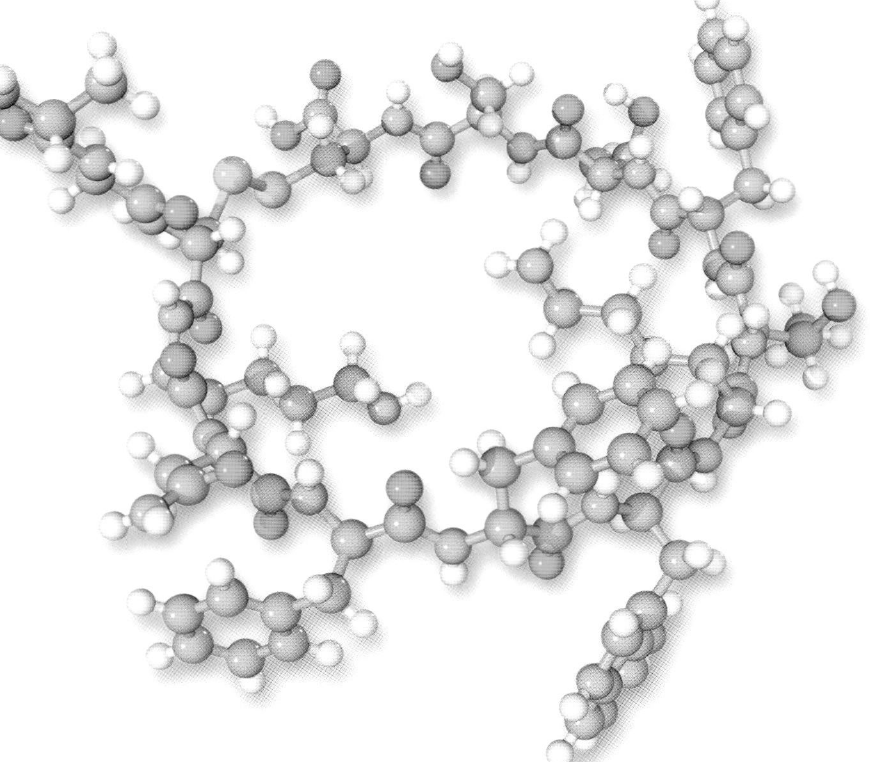

Growth inhibitor
Somatostatin is a growth-inhibiting hormone secreted mainly in the hypothalamus and the intestine. French-born physiologist Roger Guillemin identified the hormone in 1970, building on theories proposed a decade earlier by the English anatomist Geoffrey W. Harris. The structure of the first of the hormone's five receptors was revealed by molecular cloning in 1992.

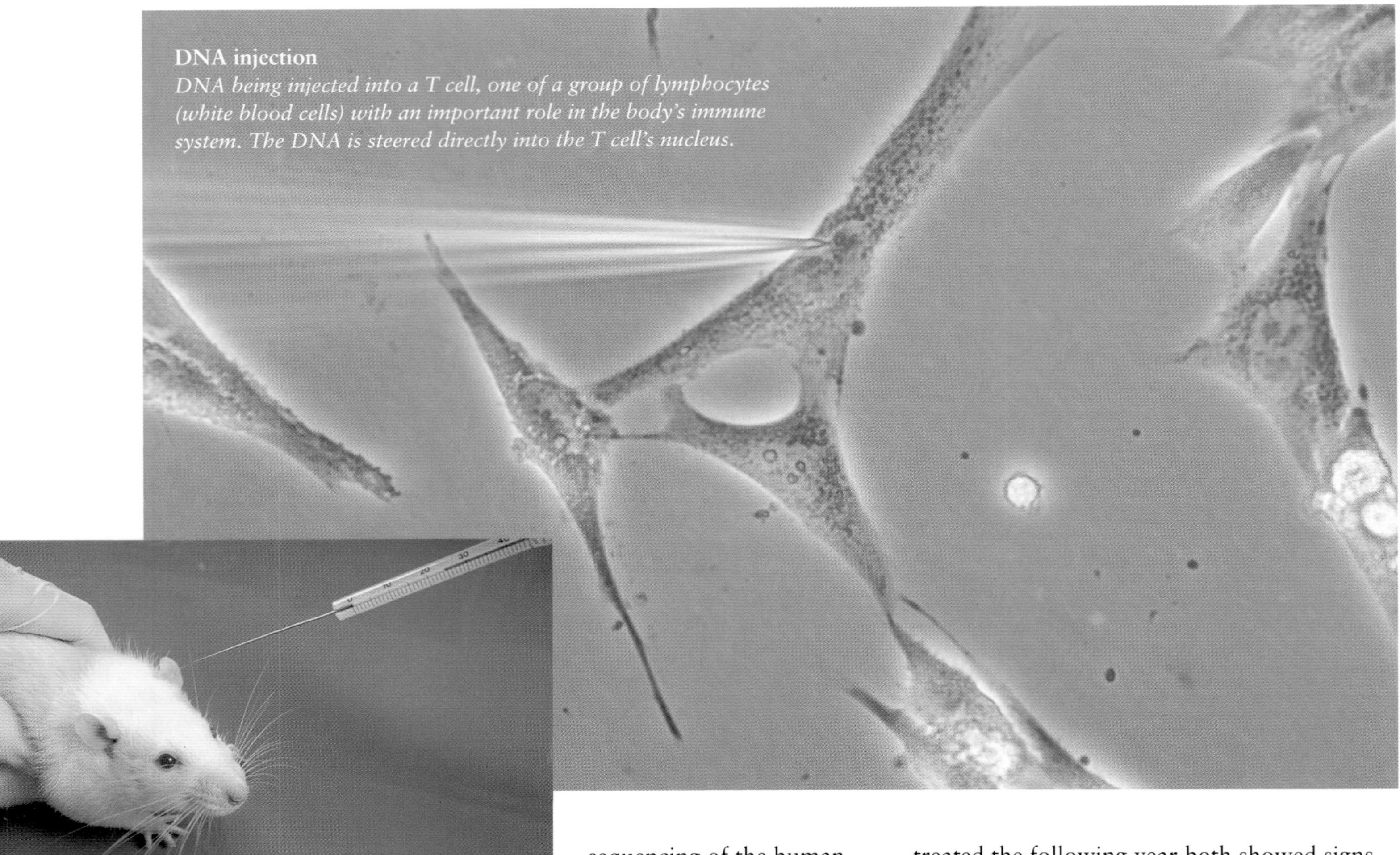

DNA injection
DNA being injected into a T cell, one of a group of lymphocytes (white blood cells) with an important role in the body's immune system. The DNA is steered directly into the T cell's nucleus.

Lab rat
Rats and mice bear some genetic and physiological resemblance to humans, and so are often used as laboratory animals.

sequencing of the human genome that substantial numbers of the genes involved in many diseases were identified.

The ADA gene was one of the first to be decoded back in 1985, and it was possible to use chemical synthesis to make a copy of it. William Anderson and his colleagues found that cells deficient in ADA could be 'healed' in culture with the help of a modified virus bearing the enzyme's gene. In 1987 experiments on monkeys confirmed the significance of the discovery. Yet when the researchers carried out the 1990 clinical trial, few people expected them to succeed. In the event, the results were ambiguous: the original four-year-old patient and a nine-year-old girl treated the following year both showed signs of improvement, but they were also being treated by the PEG method. It was not certain which therapy was doing the most good.

GERMLINE GENE THERAPY

In some cases, treating people by correcting a defective gene will not stop them from passing the malady on to their children. Researchers have therefore suggested also treating the germline, which includes the sex cells (ovocytes and spermatozoa), or else the fertilised egg, as is done in the case of transgenic animals and plants. In either case the aim would be that all a new-born baby's cells would be 'corrected'. But this method poses significant ethical questions, as it risks altering the child's inheritance through the paternal line, and with it the possibility of further genetic changes.

The shortcomings of in vivo therapy

Exciting therapeutic possibilities opened up in the course of the 1990s, but many practical difficulties remained. Most genetic ailments – for example, neuromuscular conditions – need to be treated in vivo (within living organisms) rather than ex vivo (outside the body). But no-one knew the exact amount of corrected genes that needed to be injected into a patient's blood or muscle to achieve the best effect. Since the target cells are invariably a long way from the point where the needle goes in, much of the injected material risks being lost along the way, and while it is certainly possible to correct a large number of cells, the modified cells need to remain viable over a long period of time, without fresh treatment being needed. The use of viral vectors always risks provoking an uncontrolled immune reaction, and this risk increases if the treatment has to be repeated. In short, no-one could be sure where to insert the corrected genes, which might or might not activate some other significant gene, with unforeseeable consequences.

TRANSGENIC ANIMALS

Gene therapy builds on transgenesis, a technique originally used on micro-organisms in the early 1970s, then applied more generally to plants and animals over the course of the following decade. In animals it involves injecting a DNA molecule from the same or a different species into an embryonic cell, either directly or via a vector. Transgenesis is hereditary, for the germline cells that produce the adult animal's sex cells are themselves genetically modified.

In mice the gene is injected with the aide of a tiny pipette into an egg immediately after it has been fertilised; it is then necessary to check that the foreign DNA has been inserted into the egg's genome. A team at Harvard led by Jon Gordon and Frank Ruddle managed to do this in 1980 with a viral gene. Next, the modified cell – the future embryo – must be implanted in the uterus of a pregnant mouse. In October 1981 another team, this one led by Thomas Wagner and Janice Gault at the University of Ohio, showed that a transferred rabbit gene flourished in mice and was duly transmitted to their offspring. One month later, Ralph Brinster and Richard Palmiter, working in Philadelphia and Seattle, achieved the same result using a viral gene. The following year they went further by producing giant transgenic mice that carried a rat's growth-hormone gene.

Since that time transgenic techniques have been applied to most bred species of animal including mammals, birds and fish. It is possible to create transgenic mice that suffer from close to exact replicas of human diseases, so they can be studied in laboratory conditions. Therapeutic proteins can also be produced from rabbits, pigs, sheep, cows or goats, usually in their milk, or from chickens in the whites of their eggs. The first therapeutic protein extracted from goats' milk was marketed in Europe in 2006; called ATryn (the AT is short for antithrombin), it stops blood from clotting.

Mutant mouse
Genetic modification deprived this mouse of hair and gave it thick, wrinkled skin.

Genes can also be deactivated in mice, using a technique that can be applied to xenografts – transplanted animal cells intended to make up for the lack of human organ donors. By deactivating certain animal-cell genes in such a way that they are not picked up by the human immune system, it is possible to reduce the risk that they will be rejected by the recipient. This technique, known as homologous recombination, is still in the experimental stage.

Frankenstein fish
The GloFish® is a zebrafish genetically modified by a gene extracted from a jellyfish that produces fluorescence. It can look orange in natural light and fluorescent in ultraviolet conditions.

DNA sample
A DNA precipitate extracted from cells and purified for use in experiments. It will be replicated using the polymerase chain reaction technique, then subjected to electrophoresis and sequencing.

Deciphering the code
A researcher studies the sequencing of the four DNA bases, A, T, G and C, as part of the search for the cause of Crohn's disease – a chronic inflammatory disease of the intestines (right). Several genes have been implicated in the condition.

Tragic trials

In September 1999 an 18-year-old patient named Jesse Gelsinger died in the course of a gene therapy trial in Philadelphia, USA. The young man was suffering from a fairly serious case of a hereditary liver disease called ornithine transcarbamylase deficiency or OTCD, but he was not expecting to derive any medical benefit from the procedure as the trial was intended to test the safety of the method rather than its medical efficacity. He died four days later of massive organ failure, brought on by a lethal immune response to the modified adenovirus used as a vector for the corrected gene. The inquest into his death was highly critical, ruling that he should have been excluded from the trial on health grounds and that the dose of the virus he had been given was too strong. It emerged that he had not been informed of the death of two monkeys in the course of a preceding experiment.

In 2003 gene therapy clinical trials were once more brought to a temporary halt when it was discovered that five children who had been treated in hospitals in Paris and London for severe immunodeficiency conditions had developed a form of leukaemia; it was thought that the insertion of corrected genes had somehow activated another gene implicated in causing the cancers.

A future full of promise

But gene therapy is here to stay. Other 'bubble boys' have been successfully treated at the Necker Hospital in Paris by a team under the direction of Alain Fischer and Marina Cavazanna-Calvo, while teams led by Adrian Trasher in London and Maria Roncarolo in Milan have also achieved good results in strengthening the immune system of young patients. In late 2009 a team led by Patrick Aubourg and Nathalie Cartier at the St Vincent de Paul Hospital in Paris claimed a world first for ex vivo gene therapy in treating two children suffering from a lethal brain condition

A WIDE RANGE OF USES

The principal application of gene therapy today lies in treating the 6,000 or so monogenic genetic disorders, so-called because they can be traced to a single mutated gene. Further down the line are treatments for cardiovascular diseases and cancers, conditions that involve several different genes. Of the 1,500 gene-therapy trials conducted on humans since 1989, 65 per cent have been in connection with forms of cancer.

called adrenoleukodystrophy (ALD). They used a new gene vector derived from a lentivirus to transfer the gene to the stem cells of the patients' bone marrow, transforming them into remedial glial cells. The patients are still doing well, with the progress of the disease having been halted for more than two years without any apparent harmful side effects.

Other successes include encouraging results in treating Parkinson's disease. In 2008 gene therapy at Moorfields Eye Hospital in London saved the sight of an 18-year-old suffering from degeneration of the retina caused by Leber's congenital amaurosis, a rare inherited eye condition. And in early 2010, trials were being carried out on beta-thalassemia cases. For the time being gene therapy is still focused primarily on these rare single-gene disorders, but it is hoped that by the 2020s gene therapy will form part of the general therapeutic arsenal, used on a case-by-case basis in the treatment of cancers, immune-system diseases, cardio-vascular complaints and other complex conditions involving genetic abnormalities.

Putting stem cells to work
Embryonic stem cells have the capacity to develop into different types of body cells. Here (right), they are becoming progenitor liver cells: cell nuclei are shown in blue, while the red shapes are the EpCAM epithelial cell adhesion molecules. Storage of stem cells requires very low temperatures and one of the most cost effective methods involves liquid nitrogen (below).

STEM CELLS

Some gene-therapy treatments aim to modify the stem cells of a patient's bone marrow, which can be transformed into blood cells in cases of beta-thalassemia or glial cells for adrenoleukodystrophy. Experimental trials have suggested that it might be possible to reprogramme adult cells – skin cells, for example – as so-called induced pluripotent stem cells, which are similar to embryonic stem cells and are capable of transforming themselves into any cell type. Once genetically corrected, they can differentiate themselves into a variety of therapeutic cells with a wide range of possible applications.

GENETIC ENGINEERING

Assessing the risks

Since the 1970s scientists have learned to identify, isolate and modify genes and to transfer them into animals, plants and micro-organisms as well as into human cells. These ways of manipulating genes and the genetic make-up of an organism are the tools of the controversial topic known as genetic engineering.

Genetic engineering lies at the cutting edge of biotechnological research, and large amounts of public and private money are being invested in it. Its applications range from the creation of transgenic organisms to the production of medicines such as insulin, passing on the way through animal cloning, gene therapy, organ transplants, and diagnosing and screening for genetic maladies. The most recent addition to the list is synthetic biology, a field of research that aims to use modifiable 'molecular bricks' to build molecules and cells.

Manipulating man?

Such work poses many moral dilemmas. From the early days, some scientists have drawn attention to the potential dangers involved. For example, when a Californian team led by Paul Berg was preparing in 1971 to insert a carcinogenic virus into the genome of a common bacterium, the virologist Robert Pollack warned of the risks that the release of the virus by the bacteria could pose to humankind and the environment. Other researchers, along with organisations such as Science for the People, have wondered whether this sort of modification might not lead to the genetic alteration of the human race, in rather the same way that the work of nuclear physicists led to the atom bomb. Such fears inspired 11 leading scientists to call for a moratorium on genetic engineering research in 1974 and 1975.

Since then the possible risks to human health and the environment associated with genetic engineering have continued to cause concern, most volubly in the controversies surrounding genetically modified foods. In the 1990s, such worries led to the European Union putting in place, as a precaution, a risk-assessment procedure for the civil authorities to use in cases when scientists had doubts about an innovation.

Integrity under threat

Genetic engineering also raises philosophical and ethical questions, for it touches on some fundamental values and rights. The very existence of genetically modified organisms suggests that it might be possible to modify all kinds of living creatures – a contentious prospect for those who believe that other organisms should be treated with the same respect as human beings. Another question concerns patents taken out on intellectual property involved in genetic innovations; the worry is that living genes forming part of the common heritage of humankind could end up effectively appropriated for private use.

Make-up of a mouse
The diagram below represents the chromosomes of a mouse, colour-coded for different strands of DNA.

THE ASILOMAR CONFERENCE

In February 1975 the US geneticist Paul Berg organised a conference at Asilomar State Beach, California, to survey recent advances in the nascent science of genetic engineering. It was attended by 140 molecular biologists from a number of different countries, who discussed the risks associated with genetic science and the precautions that needed to be taken to meet those risks. The result was a series of voluntary guidelines, put in place in 1976, that were intended to prevent genetically modified organisms from contaminating the environment. The procedures laid down are still in place in the developed world today, but they cannot entirely eliminate the danger of private laboratories creating biological weapons beyond the control of the public authorities.

Eco warriors at work
In April 2000, masked militants opposed to the planting of genetically modified crops destroyed an oil-seed rape (colza) crop in the Ariège region of France before it could pollinate (above).

Science-fiction fantasies
The rise of genetic engineering has fired the imaginations of both fans and creators of science fiction. This imaginary creature, called Dren (right), is the part-human, part-animal heroine of Vincenzo Natali's 2009 film Splice. *Others have dreamed of creating chromosome pills (below) to improve people's health, appearance and IQ.*

More prosaically, but equally worrying, since the 1980s genetic engineering companies have begun to promote the idea that genes linked to particular human qualities, such as intelligence or disease resistance, might be identified, replicated and injected into human embryos to improve the prospects of unborn children. Others have suggested screening embryos to detect the presence or absence of certain genes. Several US biotechnology firms are already offering screening tests, legal in some states, that claim to detect DNA sequences associated with heightened risks of developing specific illnesses. There are real dangers presented by such unsupervised genetic profiling, carried out without the support of back-up counselling, particularly if the results – which by their nature are inevitably highly confidential – should find their way to third parties such as employers or insurance companies.

THE SPACE TELESCOPE – 1990

An eye in space

The images from the Hubble Space Telescope have changed our view and understanding of the universe. But the telescope, placed in orbit in 1990, had a deeply disappointing beginning: it would take another three years and a dramatic rescue mission before the Hubble delivered on its promise.

On 24 April, 1990, the space shuttle *Discovery* left the launch pad at Cape Canaveral, Florida, carrying a very special 11-tonne payload: a cylinder measuring 13m (43ft) long by 2.4m (8ft) across. This was the Hubble Space Telescope (HST), named for the US astronomer Edwin Hubble (1889–1953), who had first demonstrated the existence of galaxies other than our own. The telescope would, in its turn, give us another new perspective on the cosmos.

The story began in 1946 when American theoretical physicist Lyman Spitzer, then a young researcher at Yale University, published an article entitled 'Astronomical Advantages of an Extra-terrestrial Observatory'. He laid out all the arguments for a telescope in space. Beyond the Earth's atmosphere the night sky is always cloudless, so the view from a telescope would be unimpeded. The light of the stars is not distorted by turbulence, providing a uniquely clear view. In addition, the Earth's atmosphere absorbs X-rays and much infrared radiation with the result that bodies emitting light in those wavelengths are invisible from the planet's surface: the space observatory that he proposed would see things in the universe that it is not possible to see from Earth. What Spitzer sketched out was nothing less than a working draft of the Hubble and of the other space telescope missions to come.

A long gestation

Spitzer wrote his article before even the first satellites had been placed in space. It took vast reserves of patience and dogged obstinacy on the part of the scheme's backers, not to mention huge amounts of money, to get an object as fragile as a telescope into orbit. In 1966 the first of four telescopes of the Orbiting Astronomical Observatory was launched, opening the way for the Hubble. These earlier telescopes observed the universe in the infrared, X-ray and gamma ray spectra. The third of the series, Copernicus, went into orbit

ANATOMY OF THE HUBBLE SPACE TELESCOPE (HST)

More than just a telescope, the Hubble is a spacecraft in its own right, orbiting the Earth every 97 minutes. Two large solar panels provide the 2,800 watts of electricity needed to power the HST's various scientific and navigational instruments; batteries take over to cover the periods when the craft moves through the Earth's shadow. The HST's 'brain' consists of two computers, one handling contact with the Earth through four antennae while the other controls all of the craft's various functions, including image capture, steering and routine maintenance. To focus in on objects that researchers want to investigate, the HST relies on a gyroscope, sensors that indicate its position in space, and three reaction wheels that manoeuvre the vessel. The HST cannot make use of the small chemical reactors used in other satellites, because the escaping gas would affect its observations, so it relies instead on momentum wheels that rotate a heavy mass around a central axle, serving to orientate the telescope in three different directions. The images are taken by charge-coupled device (CCD) cameras and stored in the on-board computer for transmission back to Earth.

Building the Hubble
The commission to build the vessel in which the telescope was to be housed (far left) went to Lockheed's Missile and Space division in Sunnyvale, California. Another company, Perkin-Elmer of Danbury, Connecticut, was put in charge of the optics. Two of Perkin-Elmer's technicians are seen here inspecting the primary mirror (left). Above: the completed HST in orbit.

in 1972 and remained in service for nine years, providing images of unprecedented clarity of more than 500 stars and galaxies.

The year 1966 also saw the first meeting of a committee, created by the US National Academy of Sciences and chaired by Spitzer, which was charged with developing the Large Space Telescope. Three years later its members published a report that stressed the urgent need of astrophysicists to have just such an instrument to observe the cosmos. The main problem lay in getting it into orbit, with the further complication of the need for maintenance missions, which presupposed easy access to space.

At this point another project, this one the brainchild of NASA, gave the space telescope idea the impetus it needed to become reality. The champions of the Large Space Telescope had realised, in effect, that the best way of delivering the instrument would be to carry it in the hold of a reuseable, rocket-powered spacecraft that could also be used to make the maintenance trips. By 1970 NASA was drawing up preliminary plans for the Space Shuttle programme. The two projects fed off one another, with proponents of one giving support to the other. In 1971 NASA's deputy administrator George M. Low gave the shuttle the go-ahead.

By 1977 the contours of the Hubble project had been defined and its goals outlined. NASA's engineers envisioned an instrument 13m long weighing 12 tonnes, with a primary mirror 3m (10ft) in diameter that was expected to deliver an unparalleled view of galactic and extra-galactic objects as much as 10 billion light-years from Earth. But the US Senate was daunted by the huge cost of the project, estimated at $500 million. As a result, the mirror's dimensions were reduced to 2.4m. At the

INFRARED VISION – A REVELATION FOR ASTRONOMERS

Space telescopes have revolutionised infrared observation of the universe. This part of the electromagnetic spectrum, which is associated with heat, is trapped by gas molecules in the Earth's atmosphere and so is largely invisible to ground-based instruments. The information that can be obtained from it mostly concerns the formation of stars, which are born in a cocoon of gas and dust that cuts out visible light, effectively hiding what is happening. But the burgeoning stars heat the clouds surrounding them, which retransmit the energy in the form of infrared radiation, brilliantly illuminating the cocoons, which would otherwise remain dark. By revealing the infrared picture, space telescopes have enabled astrophysicists to study star nurseries that would otherwise have remained hidden from view.

Lift-off

At 8.33 on the morning of 24 April, 1990, the space shuttle Discovery *blasted off (right) with five astronauts on board to put the Hubble Space Telescope into orbit (above).*

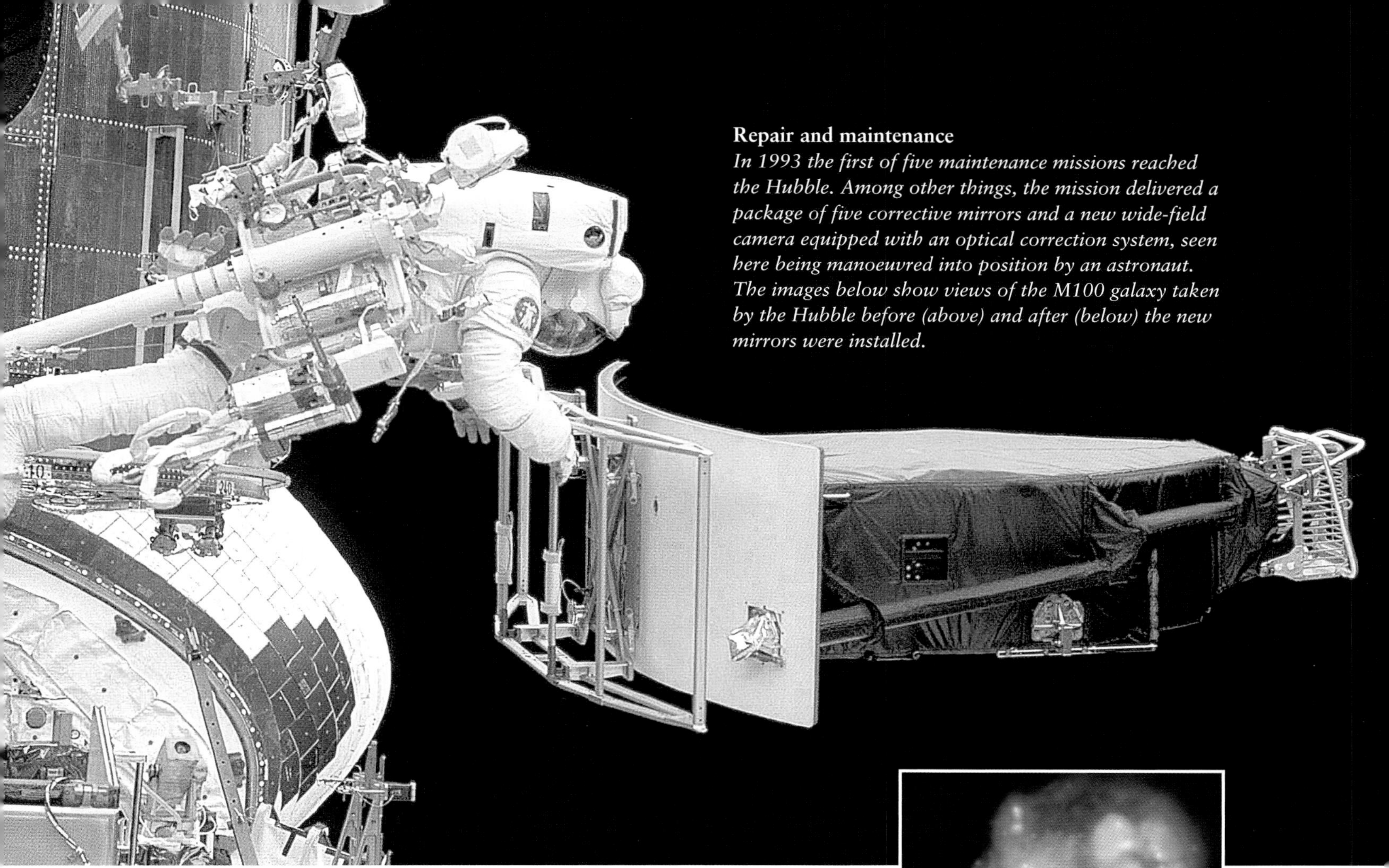

Repair and maintenance
In 1993 the first of five maintenance missions reached the Hubble. Among other things, the mission delivered a package of five corrective mirrors and a new wide-field camera equipped with an optical correction system, seen here being manoeuvred into position by an astronaut. The images below show views of the M100 galaxy taken by the Hubble before (above) and after (below) the new mirrors were installed.

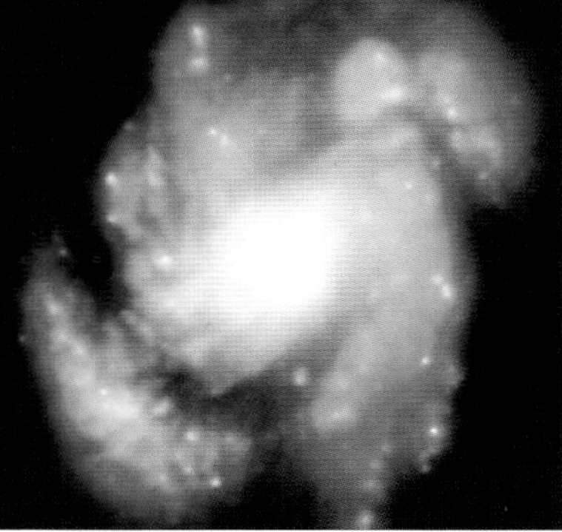

IN SPACE TELESCOPES' SIGHTS

One of the mysteries of astrophysics, gamma-ray bursts take the form of brief flashes associated with huge explosions appearing in random parts of the sky. As many as 100 such bursts may be detected in a single year. Although they reach the Earth in a weakened state, they still possess considerable energy – so much so that astronomers have long puzzled over their possible origin. Even though the details of the phenomenon are still not fully understood, it is now generally accepted that massive stars emit these bursts of energy at the end of their life, when they are collapsing in on themselves to become black holes. The discovery would not have been made without the data provided by space telescopes, notably NASA's Swift, launched in 2004, which made it possible to trace the bursts to their point of origin and to verify, in visible light, that they were linked to exploding stars.

same time, European nations were invited to lend their support to the project, providing among other things the craft's solar panels. Construction finally got under way in 1978.

A bitter twist of fate

The launch was originally planned for 1983, but the programme soon suffered delays. The optical work involved was particularly delicate; the primary mirror, for example, had to be polished to a degree of precision measured in tenths of millimetres. The telescope was finally assembled in 1985, with the launch planned for October of the following year. At this point, an unforeseen tragedy led to the Hubble spending four years in a Californian aircraft hangar: in January 1986 the space shuttle *Challenger* blew up just after take-off, killing its crew and grounding the shuttle programme. It would be two and a half years before another shuttle was launched into space. The Hubble's turn finally came in 1990, when it was placed in an elliptical low-Earth orbit 560km (350 miles) above the surface of the planet.

Celestial companions
The Whirlpool (M51A) in the Canes Venatici (Hunting Dogs) constellation is a double galaxy, whose spiral arms are in gravitational interaction with another, smaller companion. This image digitally combines a photograph taken from a telescope at the Kitt Peak Observatory in Arizona with one from the Spitzer Space Telescope.

THE LAGRANGE POINTS

The Hubble's successor, the James Webb Space Telescope (JWST), will be positioned at a very specific point in space known as L2. The 'L' stands for Joseph Lagrange, the Franco-Italian mathematician after whom the points are named. Lagrange points are places where the combined gravity fields of the Earth and the Sun come together to cancel out centrifugal force. At this tipping point, the Sun, the Earth and L2 are not only in alignment but are always fixed in relation to one another. There are five Lagrange points in all, but L2 is the closest to the Earth, at a distance of 1.5 million kilometres (930,000 miles). In this location the JWST will revolve in such a way that neither the Earth nor the Sun will seem to move at all as seen from it. It will be positioned to provide a line of sight that avoids both celestial objects.

From disappointment to triumph

The first images that the Hubble sent back to Earth seemed to live up to expectations, but after a month engineers noticed a problem: the stars it pictured were regularly surrounded by haloes. An enquiry established that the mirror had been ground to microscopically the wrong shape; in addition, the solar arrays were malfunctioning and one of the gyroscopes had broken down. Though the images were interesting, they were a bitter disappointment to those who had championed the telescope and looked forward to what it would reveal. The project risked being discredited entirely.

NASA responded by transforming the first maintenance flight into a rescue mission. On 2 December, 1993, the shuttle *Endeavour* took off from Cape Canaveral in an atmosphere of mounting tension. On board was a corrective package of mirrors which the astronaut team would install to fix the flaw in the original mirror. They would also change the HST's solar panels. Neither task had been attempted before, but the mission was a resounding success. The Hubble's images became crystal clear and the telescope went from white elephant to the stuff of legend. Since early 1994 millions of people around the world have looked with wonder at the staggering images it has provided, which have been widely distributed since the early days of the Internet. Shuttles have subsequently made four more maintenance trips to the telescope, most recently in 2009 when fresh instruments were installed to meet changing requirements.

A constellation of observatories

Although Hubble remains the iconic space telescope, it is far from the only instrument studying the universe on wavelengths outside the Earth's optical window. Uhuru, launched by NASA in 1970, helped to produce the first catalogue of X-ray sources in outer space – stars or black holes emitting huge amounts of energy. IRAS, a joint project of NASA and European space agencies, surveyed the sky on infrared wavelengths, as did ISO, a European Space Agency (ESA) project launched in 1995, NASA's Spitzer (launched in 2004) and ESA's Herschel (2009), all of them intended to give astronomers a better understanding of star formation.

The James Webb Space Telescope (JWST), named after a former NASA administrator, was planned to take over from the Hubble in 2014, a deadline that has slipped to a projected 2018. It is hoped that JWST's 6m (20ft) mirror will reflect images from the outer limits of the universe, capturing details of the very first galaxies formed just after the Big Bang. The results will be transmitted in infrared, the portion of the spectrum that the JWST is primarily equipped to explore, so the pictures that it sends back to Earth will most likely be of more interest to scientists than to the public at large. As for the Hubble, it will be taken out of orbit to reduce space clutter and will burn up as it reaches Earth's atmosphere, just like a shooting star – a fittingly spectacular end to a career that will have lasted for a quarter of a century.

THE SCIENTIFIC TALLY

No other man-made instrument has provided as much data about the heavens as the Hubble. Among its great successes were the views it provided of Comet Shoemaker-Levy crashing into Jupiter in July 1994, which gave astronomers the chance to study the gas giant's atmosphere. By sending back images of distant galaxies, the telescope has helped to lift the veil on the formation and growth of stars, and it has also shown that most galaxies have a super-massive black hole at their heart. Hubble has played a part in new fields of astronomy such as the study of exoplanets – planets outside the Solar System. In August 2009 it provided data on objects that formed within 600 million years of the Big Bang, located some 13 billion light-years away from Earth.

A view from HST *The galaxy cluster Abell 1689 (above) in the constellation Virgo lies 2.2 billion light-years from Earth.*

Hubble's replacement *An artist's impression of the James Webb Space Telescope (left), currently in development as a joint venture by NASA and the European and Canadian space agencies.*

EXTINCTION OF THE DINOSAURS

Death from the skies

For more than a century science had sought to explain the sudden disappearance, some 65 million years ago, of every known species of dinosaur. A theory, first put forward in 1980, is now generally accepted: that their extinction was the result of a massive meteorite hitting the Earth.

Dinosaurs first appeared on the planet some 230 million years ago, in the Triassic era. They survived the Jurassic and Cretaceous periods unscathed, colonising every continent. Their demise some 65 million years ago was as sudden as their reign on Earth had been long, and for many years it remained something of a mystery to palaeontologists. Then in 1980 Walter Alvarez, a geologist at the University of California's Berkeley campus, and his father Luis Alvarez, a 1968 Nobel physics laureate, proposed a scenario that seemed to come straight out of a disaster movie.

What they suggested was that, at the junction point between the Cretaceous and the Tertiary eras, the impact of a gigantic meteorite striking the Earth sent up a huge cloud of dust into the atmosphere that caused a general drop

The dinosaurs and their nemesis
Possibly the biggest dinosaur that ever existed, reaching 25m (80ft) in length, Bruhathkayosaurus *was a peaceful herbivore (above). The meteorite impact that caused its downfall – and that of all other dinosaurs – created a crater that surrounds the present-day Mexican town of Chicxulub in the north of the Yucatan Peninsula. This artist's impression (below) shows the Chicxulub crater as it may have looked 65 million years ago, shortly after the meteorite struck.*

MASS EXTINCTIONS

Besides the extinction event that wiped out the dinosaurs, scientists have identified four other mass extinctions that took place earlier in the Earth's history: the Ordovician-Silurian extinction some 439 million years ago; the Devonian extinction 365 million years ago; the Permian-Triassic 252 million years ago; and the Late Triassic extinction between 199 million and 214 million years ago.

in temperature. Deprived of sunlight for months on end, plants died, and herbivores and carnivores followed in their wake. According to the Alvarez theory, up to 80 per cent of animal and vegetable species died out over the course of just a few years.

The father and son team backed their argument with solid geological evidence that they had unearthed in the late 1970s at Gubbio in Italy. They had discovered high concentrations of iridium – a metal that is very rare on Earth but common in extraterrestrial objects – on the border between layers known to date from the Cretaceous and Tertiary periods. The two men came to the conclusion that the only possible explanation for the presence of iridium was the arrival on Earth of a giant meteorite. In the course of the 1980s some 40 other sites showing the same anomaly were discovered, reinforcing the case for the meteorite hypothesis. Today 110 such sites are known, scattered across the planet.

Great ball of fire
An artist's impression of a meteorite entering the Earth's atmosphere.

Identifying the crater

Confirmation came in 1991, when the point of impact was located at Chicxulub in Mexico's Yucatan Peninsula. Erosion and tectonic movements had previously kept it hidden, but geologists discovered quartz rocks showing evidence of extreme deformations that could only be explained by the violent impact of an extraterrestrial body. They dated these layers precisely to the Cretaceous–Tertiary boundary.

Geological research backed up by satellite images indicated that the crater was more than 200km (125 miles) across, making it one of the biggest on Earth. To hollow out a hole of that size, the meteorite must have been huge – about 10km (6 miles) across and weighing almost 1 thousand billion tonnes. Impacting at 50,000km/h (30,000mph), it would have released energy equivalent to the blast of 10,000 atomic bombs, provoking the fifth mass extinction in the Earth's history (see box, left). The creatures that survived, such as tortoises and amphibians, were better adapted than the dinosaurs to low temperatures and darkness. The same was true of the small rodents and now extinct mammal-like reptiles that would usher in the age of mammals.

A HOSTILE RECEPTION

When Luis and Walter Alvarez published their theory in 1980, it met with fierce criticism. At the time two other scenarios had been put forward to explain the Cretaceous–Tertiary extinctions. One held that over a period of half a million years huge volcanic eruptions in India had degraded the environment with an accumulation of dust and ashes. The other maintained that a gradual drop in sea levels had caused progressive climate change that slowly modified ecosystems. Both hypotheses had less geological evidence than the meteorite theory. The resistance of the scientific community to the meteorite idea was linked to a general unwillingness to accept the catastrophic explanations for geological events that had been popular in the 19th century. Analysis of the Chicxulub crater swung the majority of opinion, but critics still pointed to a lack of dinosaur fossils immediately below the Cretaceous-Tertiary boundary. Then, in 2011, researchers from Yale discovered a triceratops horn just 12.5cm below the Cretaceous-Tertiary boundary in Hell Creek, Montana, proving that some dinosaurs were alive right up to the impact.

Armoured giant
The remains of the dinosaur known as Ankylosaurus, *found in the Gobi Desert. No complete skeleton of* Ankylosaurus *has yet been assembled because it had over 1,000 bones – more than any other known creature.*

THE CHANNEL TUNNEL – 1990

Linking Britain with the Continent

At 12 minutes past noon on 1 December, 1990, two construction workers, Robert Graham Fagg and Philippe Cozette, shook hands deep below the English Channel. Fagg was from Dover, Cozette was French, and they met 22.3km (13.9 miles) from the English coast and 15.6km (9.7 miles) from the French. Their historic greeting marked the breakthrough moment for the two teams digging the Channel Tunnel, the climax of an adventure that had been long in the making.

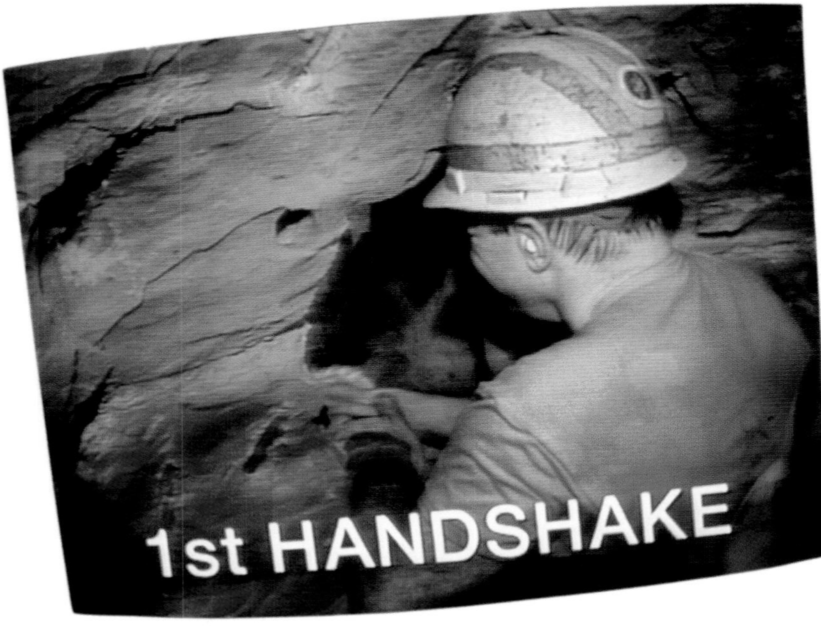

Joining hands underseas
The handshake that marked the moment when British and French tunnelling teams met up beneath the English Channel (above).

HEAVY TRAFFIC

Since its opening in 1994, more than 247 million passengers and 224 million tonnes of freight have travelled through the Channel Tunnel.

A potential project to construct a tunnel under the Channel was put forward as early as 1750. The idea was revived in 1802 by the French engineer Albert Mathieu-Favier, then in 1856 by an Englishman, William Austin. Soundings were taken in 1875 on the initiative of Aimé Thomé de Gamond and a railway tunnel more than a mile long was subsequently dug from Folkestone towards France. The work was suspended in 1883 because of British fears that invading troops could use the tunnel to reach England. The project went into cold storage until after the Second World War and it would be 1984 before the governments of the two nations finally reached agreement on the need for a cross-Channel link.

Four different proposals were considered at the time. Three of them – sponsored by Euroroute, Europont and the Channel Expressway – prioritised road traffic and envisaged the construction of either tunnels or bridges. The fourth, put forward by the Franco-British consortium Eurotunnel, stood out for its proposal to carry lorries and cars on rail shuttles. It suggested building two separate single-track railway tunnels, both 7.6m (25ft) in diameter, with a smaller service tunnel of 4.8m (15.75ft) in between, linked to the main tunnels by cross-passages at intervals of 375m (approximately every quarter of a mile). The trains employed were variations of the French high-speed TGV, adapted to fit British dimensions and platform heights. Today, they travel underground at an average speed of 160km/h (100mph).

A huge construction project

Work began in December 1987 with the sinking of two deep shafts, one on each side of the Channel, to provide access for the tunnel boring machines (TBMs). The 12 TBMs used revolved at a rate of two to four rotations a minute and the record distance tunnelled in a month was 1,718m, or a little over a mile. As the TBMs advanced, the excavated rock was removed and supports made of reinforced concrete were put into position: 720,000 curved concrete units were used to line the tunnel and keep the water out. The space between the ground rock and the lining segments was filled with cement. Guided by infrared beams, the TBMs between them pierced 148km (92 miles) of tunnel. The tunnel lining prevented them from backing up, so at the end of the project, which in all employed 12,000 engineers, technicians and labourers, they had either to be dismantled or buried.

Difficult beginnings

Construction of the tunnel was privately financed, without state aid, and the project soon ran into major financial difficulties. The costs of construction spiralled upwards from the 1987 estimate of £6 billion to nearer £12 billion. By the time the railway lines, signalling, security and ventilation systems had been installed and the tunnel was ready for its official opening on 6 May, 1994, the Eurotunnel consortium was burdened with massive debts. The company only survived thanks to financial restructuring and a government rescue operation that extended its operating concession to 2086.

Today the average journey time from London to Paris is 2 hours 15 minutes, from London to Lille 1 hour 20 minutes. A car on a rail shuttle takes 35 minutes to travel from Folkestone to Calais. Some 5,880 cars, 180 coaches, 54,000 tonnes of freight and almost 50,000 passengers use the tunnel daily.

RECORD BREAKERS

The Channel Tunnel stretches further underwater than any other submarine tunnel: 37.9km (24 miles) of the 50.5km (31 miles) between Folkestone and the French terminus at Coquelles are beneath the sea. The Seikan Tunnel in Japan, crossing the Tsugaru Strait between the islands of Honshu and Hokkaido, is longer overall at 53.85km (33.4 miles), but only 23.3km (14.5 miles) of its length passes under water. At its deepest point, the Seikan lies 240m (790ft) below sea level and 100m (330ft) below the sea-bed, as compared with 107.3m (350ft) and 40m (130ft) for the Channel Tunnel. The Eiksund undersea road tunnel in Norway is the world's deepest, reaching 287m (940ft) below sea level.

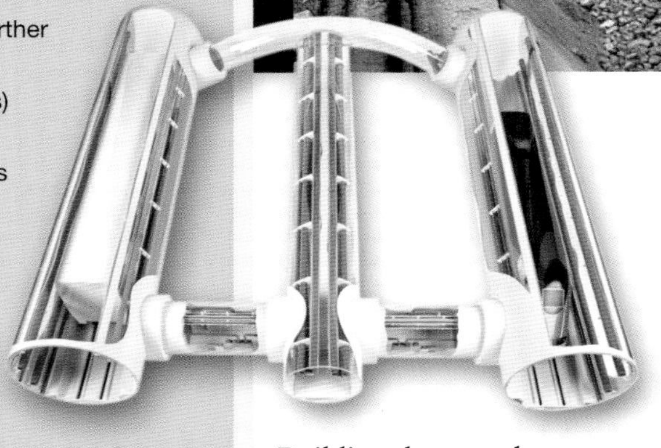

Building the tunnel
Top: a tunnel boring machine at work. Above: an artist's impression of the three linked tunnels that make up the Channel Tunnel.

Emerging into the light
A Eurostar train emerges from the tunnel on the French side at Coquelles, just south of Calais. Ventilation is provided there by huge shafts sunk at Sangatte.

SERIAL BLOCKAGES

Trains using the Channel Tunnel often break down. The worst stoppage occurred in December 2009 as a result of severe snowy weather. Traffic was interrupted for several days, and thousands of passengers had to be evacuated.

SCIENCE AND DISCOVERY CENTRES

Taking science into the leisure sector

Museums of science and technology have undergone a transformation, reinventing themselves to reach out to the public. Boldly designed display spaces are mobilising new technologies, along with interactive teaching techniques and the leisure sector's cash-generating powers, to bring knowledge to life and to make learning fun.

Future vision
Designed to resemble quartz crystals, the giant Kinemax cinema (below) is the chief attraction at the Futuroscope science park in the French city of Poitiers.

Going Dutch
The science centre in Amsterdam, known as NEMO, includes a giant laboratory where visitors can try out experiments. The building (below left), which opened in 1997, was designed by the architect Renzo Piano.

Traditionally, science museums were austere places that attracted relatively few visitors, but a new approach has swept formality aside, putting forward a different kind of museum model. One of its showcases, London's Science Museum, now attracts almost 8,000 visitors a day, while the Cité des Sciences et de l'Industrie in Paris hosts almost 10,000 visitors daily.

Science in action

The new generation of science and technology centres go under a variety of names – parks, exhibition spaces, display areas – but whatever the name, they make it their business to bring to life fields of knowledge whose applications play a growing role in daily life. The Exploratorium in San Francisco, founded by the physicist Frank Oppenheimer in 1969, set the trend at a time when autonomy and creativity were the watchwords in the education field. His creation eschewed traditional collections and instead favoured a hands-on interactive approach that encouraged visitors to touch and manipulate the objects on display as well as to use their senses of smell

A SYMBOLIC ARCHITECTURE

Visitors approaching the Museum of Technology in Berlin, housed in a former rail freight depot, are greeted by the sight of a C47 Skytrain troop carrier perched on the roof. Modern architecture sits easily with former warehouses and mills. Manchester's Museum of Science and Industry, showcase of Britain's industrial past and future, was opened in 1969 on the site of the world's oldest surviving railway station at Liverpool Road. Visitors can experience 4-D Theatre with moving seats, water spray, air blast and more. These new shop-windows for science and technology look to architecture to reinforce their innovative image while preserving the heritage of human ingenuity.

Electrifying
Two children try out a Van de Graaff generator (below), a device invented in 1929 that produces static electricity. The current passes from the sphere in the bottom right of the picture through one boy to the other via their joined hands, making the hair on the heads of both boys stand on end.

and hearing. In short, they were urged to experiment, which after all is the heart of the scientific approach. At the Discovery Centre in Guildford people could shake hands with their own hologram; at Tokyo's Miraikan they could set a humanoid robot in motion; in the Universum in the German city of Bremen, they could measure wind speed in the *Türm der Lüfte* ('Tower of the Winds'). Everywhere, ingenious exhibits invited visitors to discover or rediscover the fundamental principles of optics, mechanics, electroacoustics and a host of other disciplines otherwise usually considered unappealing. At Paris's Palais de la Découverte, in a display called 'A Researcher, An Experiment', scientists from a variety of different fields re-created experiments carried out in laboratories. There, as elsewhere, staff members organised workshop sessions where they could guide, explain and direct activities for those attending.

Bringing technology to life

Most exhibition centres today still display the kind of objects that made up the patrimony of traditional museums, only now they seek to put visitors in direct contact with them. It is no longer a matter of simply exhibiting ancient scientific instruments, they must be put in context and if possible shown in working order; if that is not possible then a functioning reduced-scale model might be on show alongside. Nowadays, when natural history museums display insects, they rarely show them pinned down dead in cases; instead, they prefer

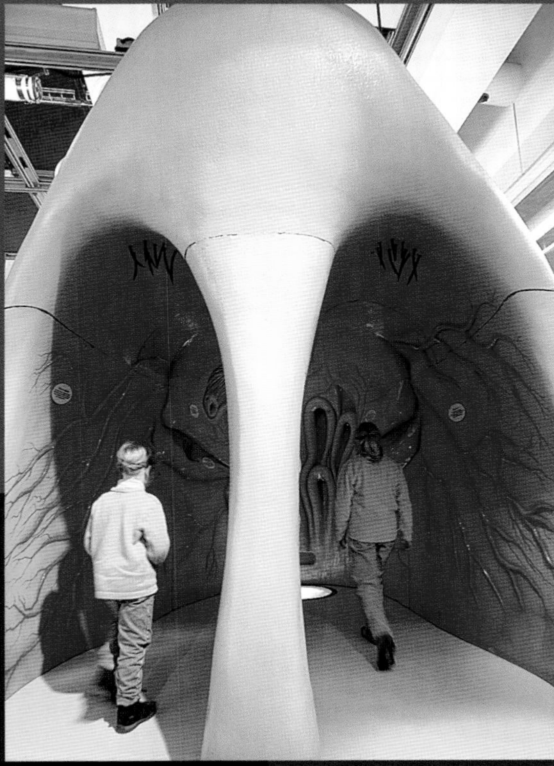

On the scent of knowledge
This giant nose was part of an exhibition called Crad'expo at the Cité des Sciences et de l'Industrie in Paris in 2004–5. The theme of the show was 'bad smells'.

ALL ABOARD

Ever since the first rack-and-pinion railways went into service carrying tourists up mountains in the 1860s, a variety of special vehicles have been used to convey passengers around visitor attractions. Theme parks took up the tradition, and science centres have followed suit. At the Epcot Center in Florida visitors travel to and from the site on a monorail train and move through the attractions Spaceship Earth and The Seas with Nemo and Friends on the Omnimover, a chain of two-seater carriages moving continuously along a sunken track. Two lateral rails swivel and tilt the carriages to orient the passengers in the direction that the designers of the exhibits intend. The vehicles in the Universe of Energy pavilion are powered by batteries charged in part by the solar panels used to roof the building.

Path to the future
The Neon Walkway, sponsored by Kodak, at the Epcot Center in Florida.

Scientist in the making
A potential future researcher plays with hydraulic circuits at the Children's Museum on Chicago's Navy Pier.

to exhibit them 'as they really are', perhaps weaver ants binding leaves together to build nests, or soldier termites protecting their queen, housed in a glass-fronted case. When real life cannot do the trick, curators turn to digital displays to illustrate more abstract concepts.

Computer screens are ubiquitous in the new science centres. For example, simulation software is used to reveal the secrets of ancient archaeological sites. At the Paléosite, a centre dedicated to prehistory near the town of Saintes in the Charente-Maritime department in western France, a Neanderthal man nicknamed Pierrette recounts his life story. Modern *Homo sapiens* visitors to the museum can use morphing software to see what they might have looked like if they had been born tens of thousands of years ago.

Science as spectacle

Technology uses images to popularise and promote science. When London's Science Museum staged *1,001 Inventions*, an exhibition on the Muslim scientific heritage, it featured a short film starring the actor Sir Ben Kingsley as al-Jazari (*c*1135–1206), inventor of a fabulous 'elephant clock'; visitors could then go on to admire a 6m (20ft) high replica of the clock. Today there is hardly a planetarium worthy of the name that does not have a 360° domed screen showing star-filled skies from other times and other latitudes, while special-effects animators take visitors on miraculous voyages to the heart of nebulae and black holes. And if even that is not enough of a draw, then why not get the hero of *Star Wars* to take part in a simulated intergalactic duel, as the National Space Centre in Leicester has done?

WALT DISNEY'S FUTURISTIC DREAM

Walt Disney originally conceived the Experimental Prototype Community of Tomorrow – Epcot for short – in the early 1950s. He planned it as the model for a new kind of city, whose inhabitants would live, work and spend their leisure time in an environment in which the most advanced technologies would help to realise a utopian vision. There would be cheap housing, jobs for all, cultural and educational facilities, and public transport that would be electrically powered at ground level while cars moved around in tunnels underground. When the centre finally opened in 1982, Disney himself had been dead for 16 years. Only a few of the elements of his initial vision survived, but the commitment to electrically-powered transport and an on-going educational and technological vocation were among them.

At the Science Museum in London, which has been engaging generations of young people with science since its foundation in 1857, the latest in IMAX 3-D technology makes it possible to accompany astronauts as they attempt the most difficult and important tasks in NASA's history. Visitors can experience exactly what it is like to fly in a space shuttle or to undertake a space walk. Then, using imagery from the Hubble Space Telescope, viewers are transported deep into the far reaches of the universe.

Nearby, at the Natural History Museum, visitors can interact with dinosaurs of all descriptions as they explore the living world past and present. In 2001 the Natural History Museum erected a huge butterfly house on its front lawn to enable visitors to interact with butterflies in five sensory zones of sight, smell, taste, hearing and touch.

The new science and technology centres have managed to marry together two worlds that by long tradition were miles apart: the traditional museum and the theme park. The Walt Disney Company was the first organisation to cross the dividing line between the two when it opened the Epcot Center at Disney World in Florida in 1982. Epcot takes visitors on a journey through the history of communications, the taming of energy, space exploration and threats to the environment. To do so it employs all the simulation and imaging technologies familiar from other Disney theme parks, as well as futuristic forms of transport that elsewhere are used to go to see Cinderella or the heroes and heroines of Disney's animated films.

A new world of science for fun

The choice today is no longer between education and recreation but rather between multiple combinations of the two. Fascinated by dinosaurs? There is a Dinosaur Adventure park in Norfolk, while Torquay has Dinosaur World promising interactive play zones and a Dinosaur Café. Interested in volcanology? At the foot of a chain of extinct volcanoes near Le Puy in the Auvergne region of France

Iconic entrance
Resembling a giant golf ball, the 60m high geodesic dome known as Spaceship Earth marks the gateway to the Epcot Center (above). It has become the symbol of the park.

Meet the ancestors
France's National Museum of Prehistory, at Eyzies-de-Tayac in the Dordogne, has life-size reconstructions like this one of Turkana Boy (below left), a hominid adolescent whose fossilised remains were found at Lake Turkana in Kenya in 1984.

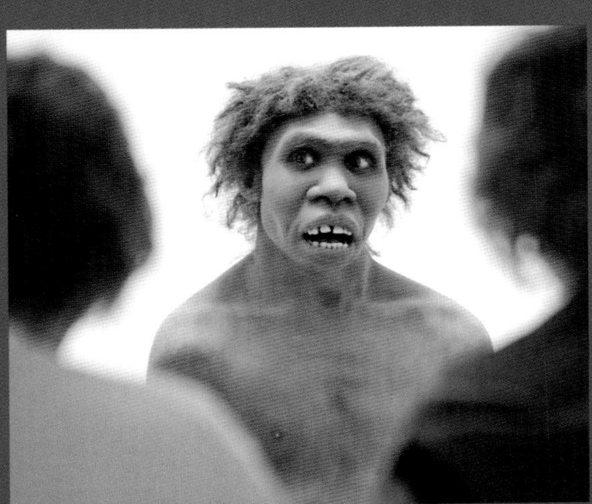

INESCAPABLE IMAX

In 1970 the first IMAX film premiered at Expo '70, held in Osaka, Japan. By horizontally unreeling a film 7cm (2.75in) wide in a projector equipped with a 15,000W light source, the system exposed 10 times more film surface than the classic 35mm format. The resolution of the images was so sharp that they could be projected onto a screen 25m (80ft) high. In 1973 IMAX cameras and projectors were fitted with fish-eye lenses that distort the image at the time of filming but reinstate the correct perspective in the projection process, when these Omnimax films are shown on a hemispheric screen. The images take up the whole of the spectators' field of vision, effectively drawing them into the film.

FROM 3-D TO 4-D

In recent years 3-D has been given a new lease of life by combining established 3-D techniques with new simulation technology. A flight simulation platform for spectators at one science park in France moves and accelerates on hydraulic jacks to link in with 3-D digital images. Another re-creates the world of the Minnimoys, fictional creatures the size of insects, taking visitors into a magic land in 25-seater carriages programmed to move on six different axes in synchronisation with 3-D film projected on an IMAX dome. To increase the thrill, special effects are deployed within the cinema to tie in with on-screen images and the stereo soundtrack. The spectators feel wind blowing in their faces, enhancing the sense of flying, and they physically feel the sensation of being brushed by the strands of a cobweb. Welcome to the fourth dimension.

Imaginary world
A ride at the Poitiers Futuroscope (above), part of a themed attraction designed by film-maker Luc Besson, based on his 2007 fantasy feature Arthur and the Invisibles.

visitors to Vulcania can hear fires rumbling under the earth and watch lava flowing. At the Eden Project, located within a disused clay pit near St Austell in Cornwall, visitors can wander through a rainforest inside a geodesic dome, all the while learning about tropical environments.

The key concept behind most projects is the illustration of a specific scientific theme. The space and content of an exhibition are no

longer organised according to scientific rules of classification, as in traditional museums, but rather to pursue the widest possible variety of approaches to knowledge. As on the Internet, visitors can surf the attractions following their own inclinations, drawn on by elaborate displays and reconstructions. At Space City in Toulouse, for instance, they can sit behind the controls of a mock-up of the Russian Mir space station that was originally used for ground testing, or experience daily life aboard the International Space Station or even, in simulation, visit distant galaxies and more.

For lovers of the oceans, aquariums and sea-life centres rival one another in the lengths they go to to show marine creatures in their natural environment. At London Zoo's new penguin pool, opened in 2011, a 200-strong breeding colony has been established for 65 of the world's most threatened breeds. For a spectacle on a grander scale, visitors to the Georgia Aquarium in Atlanta move through a translucent tunnel as whale sharks and other oceanic fauna swim around and above them. The human body and the way it works is a theme explored by many museums, whether through being able to see into your own veins at At-Bristol or by experiencing riding a bicycle with a skeleton at the Museum of Science in Boston, Massachusetts.

Children exposed to technological and scientific adventures may not end up choosing a career in the sciences. But they may well learn to see the world around them as both a less mysterious and a more magical place.

Imaginarium
Visitors to the Rose Center for Earth and Space, part of New York City's Museum of Natural History, watch a 3-D reconstruction of the Big Bang in the building's planetarium.

World beater
Since 2005 the Georgia Aquarium in the US city of Atlanta has claimed to be the biggest in the world. It is home to an estimated 100,000 fish presented in 60 different natural environments, among them this whale shark (left).

SHAKY ECONOMIC FOUNDATIONS

The establishment of a science and discovery centre involves a heavy initial investment followed by high running costs, resulting in a financial equation that is hard to balance, as attendance figures often follow a declining curve. After an initial surge in admissions, public interest tends to fall away unless revived by new attractions. In the UK, a couple of science-themed millennium projects have already fallen by the wayside. The Big Idea, built near Irvine in Scotland on the site of a former dynamite factory owned by Alfred Nobel's company, never managed to attract the 70,000 annual visitors it needed to break even; it closed in 2003. Doncaster's Earth Centre, opened in 1999, similarly shut its doors five years later. Yet other centres established at the same time are still doing well, even if few can match the success of the European sector leader, the Cité des Sciences et de l'Industrie in Paris, which attracts 3 million visitors a year.

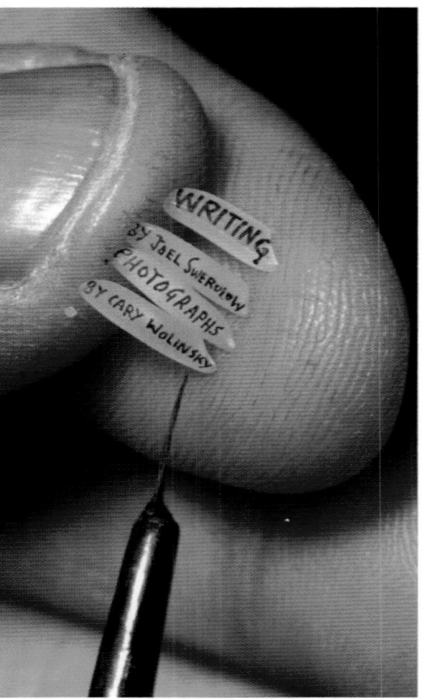

NANOTECHNOLOGY – 1991

On a scale of millionths of a millimetre

When scientists learnt how to manipulate molecules smaller in size than 100 nanometres (nm) – equivalent to 100 billionths of a metre – they took science into a new era: the age of nanotechnology. With prospects for the new technology in almost every aspect of daily life, researchers are already comparing the new field with the invention of the steam engine or the taming of electricity.

Knowledge in miniature
Grains of rice (left) are a large canvas compared to the pinhead that Richard Feynman foresaw would one day hold the entire Encyclopaedia Britannica.

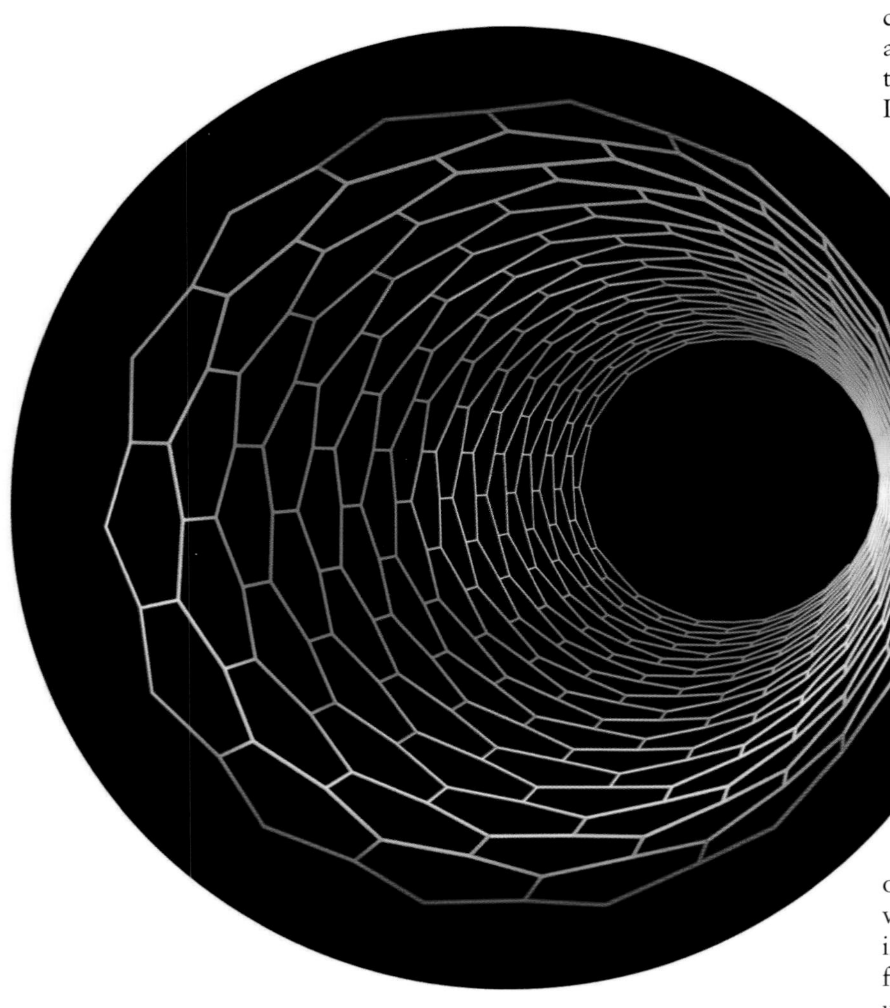

Carbon nanotube
A computer simulation of a nanotube – a cylinder made up of a single leaf of graphite consisting of a mesh of fullerene atoms organised in a hexagonal pattern.

Take a plastic tube. Wrap it in a fishing net with hexagonal mesh. Then take away the tube. In hugely magnified form, this is the shape of a carbon nanotube, a molecule that might well change everyday life. In real life a carbon nanotube is 100,000 times finer than a human hair but stronger than steel wire. The tubes were first officially identified by Sumio Iijima at the University of Tsukuba in Japan in 1991. Since then they have changed not just the face of science but of the world. From zero, the nanotechnology economy has mushroomed to not far short of £100 billion annually – a rate of growth that no-one could possibly have imagined, except perhaps for one man: Richard Feynman.

Feynman's vision

The date was 29 December, 1959, and Feynman was giving a speech to the annual gathering of the American Physical Society at the California Institute of Technology (Caltech). In a prophetic address, he announced the advent of the nanoworld. 'Why cannot we write the entire 24 volumes of the *Encyclopaedia Britannica* on the head of a pin?' he asked his bemused audience. Answering his own question, he spelled out his vision of a science that could manipulate atoms one by one – the founding principle of the various forms of nanotechnology. Feynman imagined vast future prospects for this new field, but he left it to other people to open it up, his own field of interest being primarily theoretical physics and elementary particles. He died in 1988, garlanded with honours including the 1965 Nobel prize for physics, when the revolution that he had foreseen was just about to get underway.

Turning ideas into reality

Eric Drexler, an engineer who admired Feynman's work, took up the challenge of fleshing out the master's vision. In a 1986 work, *Engines of Creation*, Drexler popularised the term 'nanotechnology', which had originally been coined in 1974 by Norio Taniguchi of the Tokyo University of Science. Also in 1986 Drexler founded the Foresight Institute in Palo Alto, California, which became the first nanotechnology research centre. At roughly the same time the US chemist Richard Smalley, a Nobel prizewinner in 1996, discovered fullerenes, molecules composed of at least 60 atoms of carbon that can take spherical, ellipsoid or tubular form. The discovery marked a giant leap forward, for up to that time scientists had believed that carbon atoms only formed hard-edged shapes based on the hexagon.

By that time the ideas had been formulated, as had the will to pursue them, but the tools needed had still to be developed. In that respect the invention of scanning tunnelling microscopes (STMs) in 1981 by two IBM employees, Gerd Binnig and Heinrich Rohrer, was decisive, enabling researchers to see objects as small as 0.2nm in diameter. With the help of these instruments and their successors, atomic force microscopes (AFMs), Donald Eigler was able in 1989 to form the initials 'IBM' by individually moving 35 xenon atoms using the ultrafine tip of the microscope head as a prod.

Feynman's intuition had proved correct – there was indeed nothing to prevent matter being moved atom by atom – and a huge new field of applications opened up for research. For the physical and chemical properties of

Colour coded
In this colorised electron microscope image of a carbon nanotube (right), the colours reveal the nanotube's structure, with successive layers of carbon atoms surrounding a vacuum measuring 15 nanometres across.

NANOCLEAN

Whether behaving actively or passively, nanoparticles offer new possibilities in the field of decontamination. In active mode, a film of nanoparticles of titanium dioxide spread on the surface of water only needs heat from the Sun in order to destroy pesticides and some micro-organisms. Passively, ceramic membranes derived from ferroxane nanoparticles can be used to filter contaminated water. In the long run technology along these lines should be inexpensive, making it a promising prospect for developing countries.

Manipulating single atoms
A researcher at IBM managed to spell out the company's initials in individual atoms (above). He moved the atoms one by one using an atomic force microscope (AFM); the movements of its cantilevered tip (right) make it possible to scan, measure and manipulate matter at the nanoscale.

RECIPE FOR A CARBON NANOTUBE

The basic steps in making nanotubes consist of vaporising graphite (a form of carbon) by heating it beyond 3,000°C and leaving it to condense. To reach temperatures that high, scientists and manufacturers use electric arcs or lasers. If the graphite is vaporised on its own, it produces multi-walled nanotubes (MWNT) made up of a number of concentric tubes in rolled layers. To produce single-walled nanotubes, a metal catalyst is required. It is possible to produce nanotubes at lower temperatures by the process known as vapour deposition. This involves placing hydrocarbons like methane or ethylene in an oven, at between 500°C and 900°C to produce multi-walled and 750–1200°C for single-walled allotropes. Using this technique, nanotubes can be 'grown' directly onto an electronic circuit.

Viewing the invisible
Fullerenes are pentagonal or hexagonal carbon molecules that take different forms, among them nanotubes (above). Below: An atomic force microscope reveals titanium dioxide nanoparticles.

matter change at a scale of only a handful of atoms, as opposed to the billions with which normal life is concerned. Gold, for example, ceases to be an inert metal as new properties come into play, allowing it to serve as a catalyst for some chemical reactions, when in theory it should remain neutral. At the nano level, rubber can conduct electricity without losing its pliability. It is hardly surprising, then, that nanotechnology fired passionate interest around the world, as expressed by the foundation of the National Nanotechnology Initiative in the USA and the priority financing the European Union accorded the new science.

Making science fiction fact

In electronics, nanotechnology makes it possible to miniaturise components. In 2007, for example, it was estimated that the number of transistors integrated into electronic parts had increased sixteenfold thanks to the new techniques. Even so, the size of integrated circuits was still measured then in tens of nanometres, which is ten times the figure today. The advent of spintronics in the 1990s allowed increased amounts of data to be stored on computer hard disks. Ever smaller and more powerful, computer chips found their way into more and more devices, televisions and washing machines among them. Almost all household white goods became 'smart'.

The amazing properties of carbon nanotubes, which proved to be six times lighter and 100 times more resistant than steel, found many uses. They served to reinforce plastic: a bullet-proof waistcoat made with them is 17 times more effective than one made of Kevlar®. Composite materials featuring nanoparticles alongside aluminium, steel or reinforced carbon–carbon gave greater resistance to rust, erosion and general wear and tear than their competitors, while also being lighter. Smart textiles can change colour and resist dirt. Car bodywork can be made scratch-resistant. Silicon nanoparticles can replace carbon black in tyres, reducing rolling resistance without harming performance. Skyscrapers can be provided with windows that clean themselves every time it rains. The list sounds like science fiction, but the fact is that all these inventions have already arrived or are about to be introduced.

SPINTRONICS

The 2007 Nobel prize for physics went jointly to the German Peter Grünberg and France's Albert Fert for their work on spintronics, an emerging science that takes as its starting point the way that electrons naturally spin. In fact, spin is an intrinsic property of a number of elementary particles, a fundamental part of their identity, just as the colour of someone's eyes is for humans. Through their work on the spin of electrons, Fert and his colleagues at Paris-Sud 11 University showed that it was possible to store information in multi-layered packages composed of very fine layers of iron just one or two atoms thick, separated by layers of chrome.

The concept of spintronics developed in the 1970s, but it was the late 1980s before researchers at the electronics firm Thomson–CSF managed to create materials with a precision of just a few nanometres. Developed on an industrial scale since the mid 1990s, spintronic techniques have made it possible in just a few years to increase the storage capacity of computer hard disks a hundredfold. Without the new technology, MP3 players and similar digital audio devices equipped with miniature hard disks would not exist.

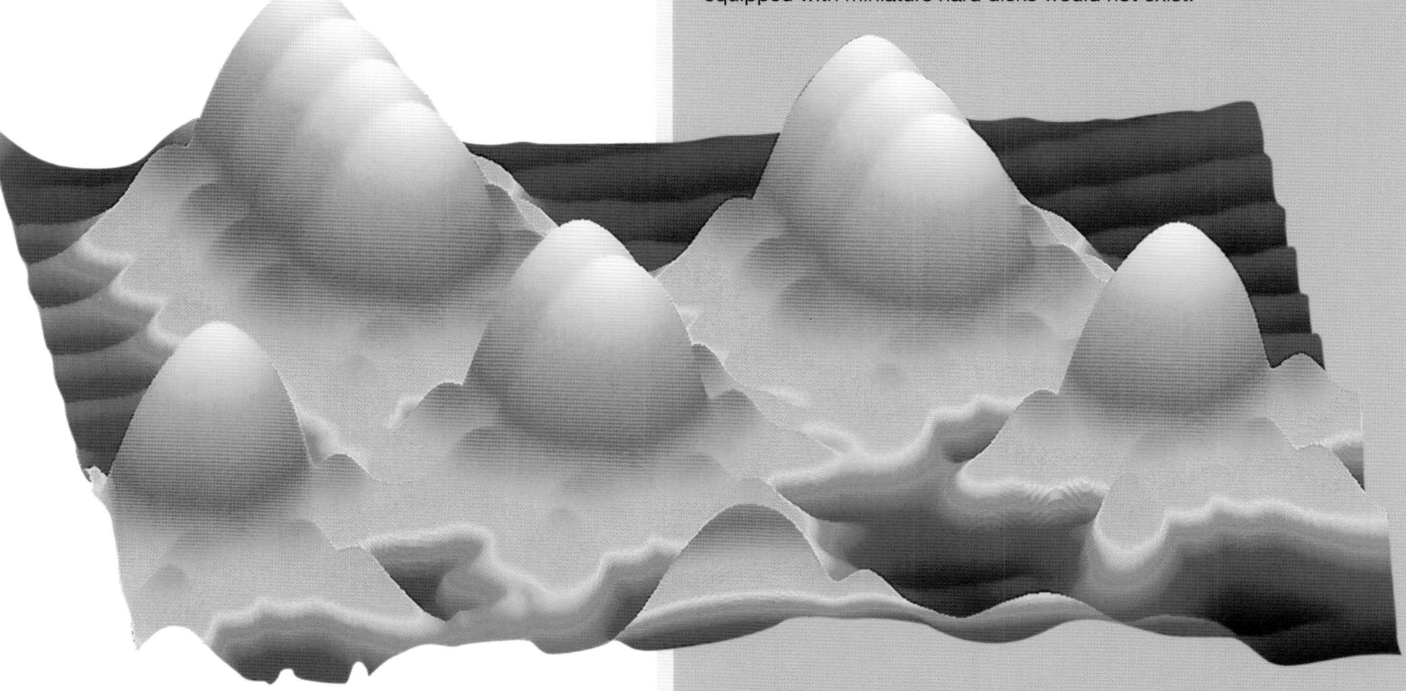

Nanomountains
When manganese atoms come into contact with a film of the semi-conductor gallium arsenide (in blue above), the electrons of the two metals (red and yellow) react violently; their rate of rotation, or 'spin', changes, creating the protrusions seen above. It then becomes possible, as A. Yazdani and D.J. Hornbaker have shown in the microscopy laboratory at Princeton University, to replace each gallium atom by a manganese atom along the length of a given circuit, using a tunnelling microscope. The result is a magnetic semi-conductor that can not just handle data but also store it. This achievement is made possible by a peculiar phenomenon of quantum mechanics, namely that electrons subjected to a certain level of agitation lose their identity.

Nanotechnology also has applications in the field of energy. Nanoparticles of aluminium added to kerosene increase the chemical reactivity of the hydrocarbon mixture tenfold, recycling energy and so making engines more fuel-efficient. Fuel cells capable of generating electricity by consuming hydrogen and oxygen, only rejecting water, are opening the way for non-polluting electric vehicles. Nanoparticles incorporated into the hydrogen reservoir increase the battery life and so the effective range of the cars.

In the field of medicine, a dozen or so treatments for a range of conditions stretching from cancer to mycoses (diseases caused by fungi) already employ nanotechnology techniques. Biodegradable nanoparticles just one-seventieth the size of a red blood cell can deliver their active ingredients directly into an affected organ, tissue or cell. Microscopic DNA probes are already foreshadowing the development of laboratories no larger than pinheads that will be able to distinguish one or more molecules present in the bloodstream and to carry out DNA tests or detect viruses in a fraction of the time that is currently needed. And surgeons will before long be able to use nanoscalpels and nanoforceps to access and cut into single cells.

Nanotechnologies and nanoscience

Nanotechnologies are already revolutionising many elements of our daily lives, but they can only continue to do so if nanoscience – which is to say the exploration of the physical, chemical and mechanical properties of matter at the submicroscopic level – develops alongside them. This is a daunting task, for on a scale of billionths of a metre matter no

Self-cleaning windows
Drops of water, like the one shown in close-up (top), attach themselves to windows made of normal glass (above left) but they cannot stick to self-cleaning glass (above right) which has nanoparticles incorporated into its surface layer.

NANOTECHNOLOGY – THE POTENTIAL RISKS

The development of nanotechnology has stirred up similar concerns to those raised by the advent of genetically modified foods. After a period of uncertainty, the authorities in Britain and continental Europe are now taking steps to address these, following the example of Canada, which first introduced a mandatory safety reporting scheme for nanotechnology companies in 2009. While some studies on rats and mice have suggested that fullerenes and nanotubes of carbon or titanium dioxide could pose a risk to living organisms, it is proving difficult to test all nanoparticles because of the numbers involved and their sheer diversity. Until an exhaustive evaluation has been made, the precautionary principle holds sway. Laboratories creating nanoparticles in aerosol form are thus being required to install filters capable of trapping 95 to 99.99 per cent of their emissions. Risks are posed in other fields, too. Nanotechnology could be used to create virtually undetectable surveillance devices to spy on governments, corporations and private citizens. Or it could be employed to create minute, untraceable weapons the size of an insect but with the intelligence of a supercomputer.

longer obeys the classic laws of physics but instead operates according to the stranger and more complex rules of the quantum realm, where huge amounts remain to be discovered. Already, however, scientists around the world are publishing tens of thousands of articles on the subject every year, while the website of the Institute of Nanotechnology, a world leader, gets a massive 1.75 million hits a month. The amount of attention paid to the new science, rich in promise as it is, also reflects the urgent need to understand and master the miniature yet boundless universe the nanoworld represents. That much is an essential precondition if nanotechnology is to realise our hopes rather than justify our fears.

NANOFOOD

Nanotechnology may soon be finding its way into our kitchens. Nanomaterials added to packaging can block the passage of water, air and ultraviolet radiation, prolonging the shelf life of food. Incorporated into dietary supplements, they can add extra vitamins. For the moment most developments are still in the realm of science fiction, but experts already reckon that nanotechnology will provide the food industry with its next step forward by modifying classic foodstuffs to give them fresh qualities, whether practical or nutritional.

Fireproofing in Saarbrücken
At the Leibniz Institute for New Materials, part of Germany's Leibniz Association of research institutes, researchers test heat-resistant glass developed with the aid of nanotechnology.

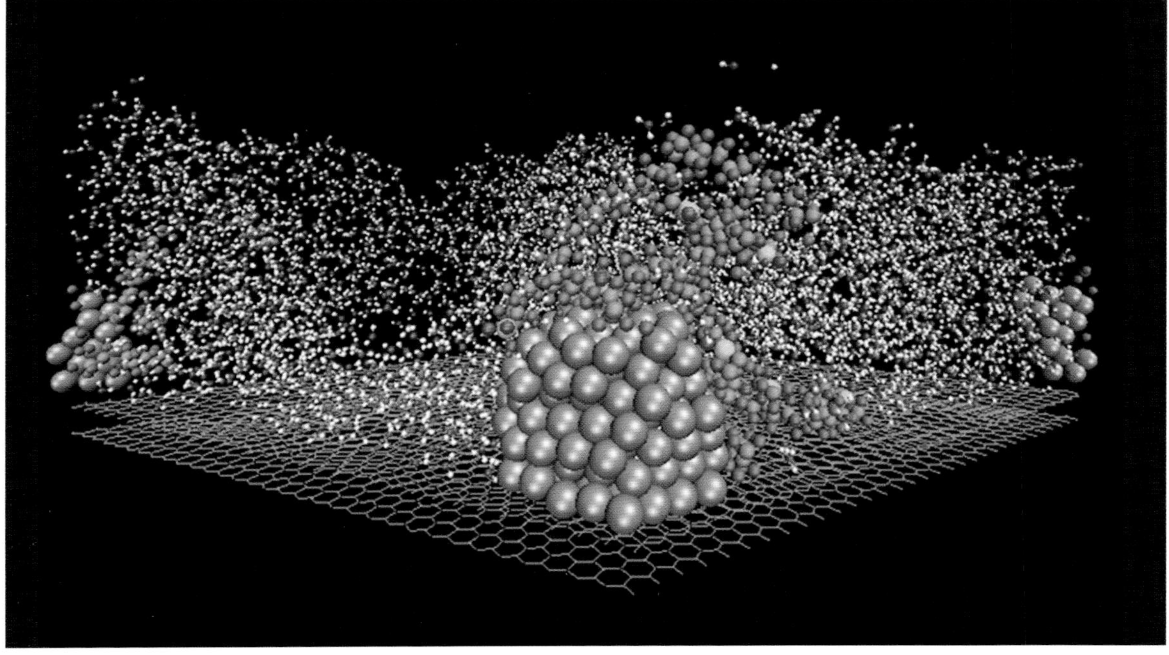

Fuel of the future *A computer simulation shows the catalytic effect that platinum nanoparticles (gold) with a carbon base (blue) have on water molecules (red and white) in the presence of Nafion nanoparticles (other colours). This reaction has valuable implications for fuel cells.*

SOLAR ENERGY

An endlessly renewable resource

In the race for clean energy, solar power has so far remained marginal, mostly because of its cost. But significant technical innovations, including polymer cells that are cheaper to produce than silicon, make it a promising alternative for the future.

Power of reflection *Reflecting surfaces like this parabolic disc (above) concentrate sunlight onto solar collectors that store it with the aid of a heat-retaining liquid. Below: The world's largest solar thermal plant, located in the Mojave Desert of California, employs parabolic trough mirrors that reflect the Sun's rays onto a central tube filled with synthetic oil.*

The dream of producing power from sunlight is an old one that people have sought to realise for thousands of years. In ancient Rome Plutarch recorded that if the sacred flame in the Temple of Vesta chanced to go out, the Vestal Virgins – priestesses of the health goddess Vesta – used mirrors reflecting the Sun's rays to relight it. Classical historians claimed that in 220 BC the Greek scientist Archimedes used giant mirrors to concentrate sunlight onto the Roman fleet besieging Syracuse, setting the ships on fire. Ancient sundials used to bear the inscription *Sol Lucet Omnibus*, 'The Sun Lights Up All'.

In effect, solar energy is the ideal power source: available practically everywhere, renewable to the point of inexhaustibility, free and non-polluting. On average, Europe receives the equivalent of 3kWh (kilowatt

hours) daily per square metre; in the hottest deserts the figure reaches 7kWh. Adding all of this up, harnessing just one thousandth part of the total amount of solar energy reaching the Earth's surface would provide more than enough energy for all the world's needs.

Thermal and thermodynamic

Three principal ways of profiting from this exceptional resource have presented themselves. Solar thermal energy means directly exploiting the heat contained in solar radiation. Water in a garden hose left in the sun warms up, the more so if the tube is dark-coloured and placed under glass, and solar thermal works on exactly the same principle. The warmth from the Sun is captured with the aid of a heat-retaining liquid, which is circulated under glass in a solar collector. The fluid then conveys the heat to a hot-water system or to the different rooms of a house. The Swiss physicist Horace-Bénédict de Saussure demonstrated this 'greenhouse effect' in the mid 18th century. In the USA, the first solar water heaters went on the market at the start of the 20th century. The concept of the solar house, planned to minimise heat loss and make the most of solar radiation through its design and the materials used, first appeared in the 1970s.

In contrast, solar thermodynamics involves transforming thermal heat into mechanical energy. The Sun's rays are concentrated to heat a liquid to a very high temperature, then the pressurised steam is used to drive turbines to produce electricity. This is the principle behind the Concentrating Solar Power (CSP) plants that have been built in the USA, India, Spain, China and France, where a pioneering facility, THEMIS, opened in the Pyrenees as early as 1975. These solar power stations have important advantages in their storage capacity and in the economies of scale available to plants with a high generating capacity.

Between them, thermodynamic plants employ four different basic technologies. The most popular involves massed ranks of solar arrays, hundreds of metres long, that focus the Sun's radiation on pipes containing heat-retaining fluid. Facilities of this kind in California have generated a total output of 354MW, a world record. Tower plants, like Spain's PS10 plant near Seville, consist of rows of mirrors that concentrate sunlight on a receiver placed at the top of the tower. The third technology involves parabolic reflectors that follow the Sun, again focusing its rays on a central collector. Finally, the most recent technological additions are chimney installations, of which a prototype was

Simple and direct
The simplest form of solar heating uses the Sun's rays to warm water in pipes on the roof that is then circulated around the building below, as in this hotel in China's Hubei province (left).

Concentrated heat
Parabolic reflectors like these ones near Almeria in Spain focus the Sun's rays on collectors positioned at their apex.

THE ODEILLO SOLAR FURNACE

The solar furnace installed at Odeillo (below), near Font-Romeu in the French Pyrenees, is among the biggest in the world, rivalled only by one near Tashkent in Uzbekistan. Brought into service in 1970, the Odeillo furnace concentrates the Sun's rays on a circular hot spot about 80cm (32in) in diameter. The rays are first trapped by an array of 63 flat tracking mirrors installed on terraces. These direct the radiation to a second series of more than 9,000 mirrors set in an immense parabola 40m (130ft) high and 54m (175ft) wide. The rays converge on the summit of the central tower, creating temperatures as high as 3,800°C (6,900°F). The installation is used to study the properties of matter exposed to high temperatures.

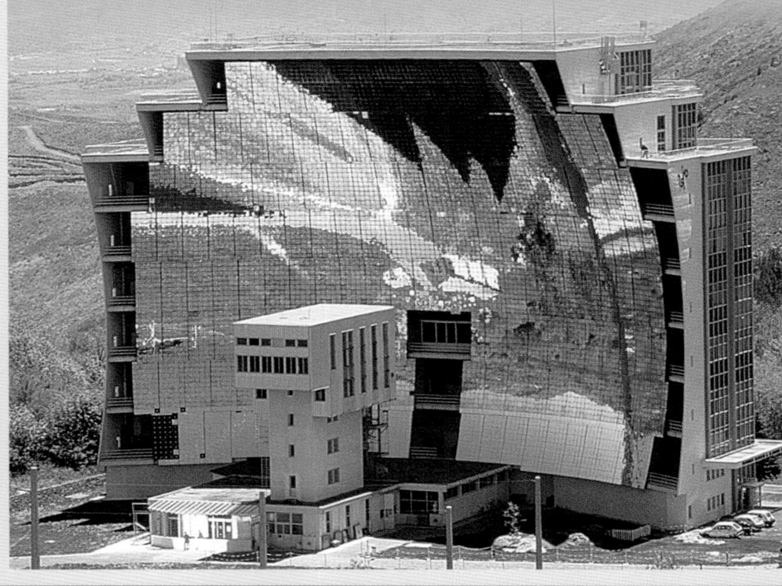

Harvesting the Sun
Located in the Mojave Desert, one of the hottest places on Earth, Solar Two was an experimental tower plant that used the heat reflected from a vast array of mirrors to turn a salt solution in the central tower to steam that was then used to power a turbine. The tower was demolished in 2009.

constructed at Stuttgart in 1982. In these, the Sun heats the air contained in a greenhouse, causing it to rise up a chimney as it becomes warmer and lighter, activating turbines that generate electricity as it does so.

Photovoltaic systems

A third type of solar power involves the photovoltaic effect, first demonstrated in 1839 by French physicist A.E. Becquerel, by which light energy is transformed into electricity. Until the Second World War, it remained little more than a scientific curiosity. Then, in 1954, three US engineers working for Bell Telephone developed a silicon photovoltaic cell with a relatively high energy yield of 6 per cent. At the time the US space industry was looking for new energy sources, and the first satellites employing the cells were launched in 1958. They were subsequently also used in unmanned probes and space stations.

Solar cells convert the sunlight they receive into electrical charges. These light-powered mini-batteries rely on semi-conductor technology, usually employing silicon in the form of two thin wafers, one classed as negative or N-type (having excess electrons) and the other positive (P-type, with no free electrons). When solar photons reach the upper wafer, they free up electrons that pass into the lower one, creating a continuous electric current. This energy can be used directly or it can be steered toward either a permanent grid or else a battery that can be used to deliver electricity when required. The individual photovoltaic cells are grouped together in solar panels in numbers designed to match the desired power output.

In the second half of the 20th century, solar panels started to appear on house roofs to heat water or generate electricity, particularly in places with good insolation (exposure to the Sun), but also in isolated regions where alternative means of providing electricity were costly. Thanks to the dependability of photovoltaic technology, it also found its way into telecommunications devices, navigation aids (in the form of land or sea-based beacons) and road safety, where it is used to activate traffic signs. Solar cells also power everyday appliances such as calculators and watches. Since the year 2000 a number of solar power stations bringing together large solar arrays to increase their generating power have opened up, and many others are being planned.

Despite such benefits, the technology has been slow to impose itself. It has faced two main handicaps: high cost of installation and relatively low yield in energy. A classic silicon cell converts only a small part of the solar energy it receives into electricity, so the size of the arrays employed has increased steadily, as has the cost of installing them. Much work

Solar panels
A solar array (below) built by BP Solar, the oil giant's solar-power subsidiary. The panels are composed of photovoltaic cells about 1mm thick (below left), made of silicon.

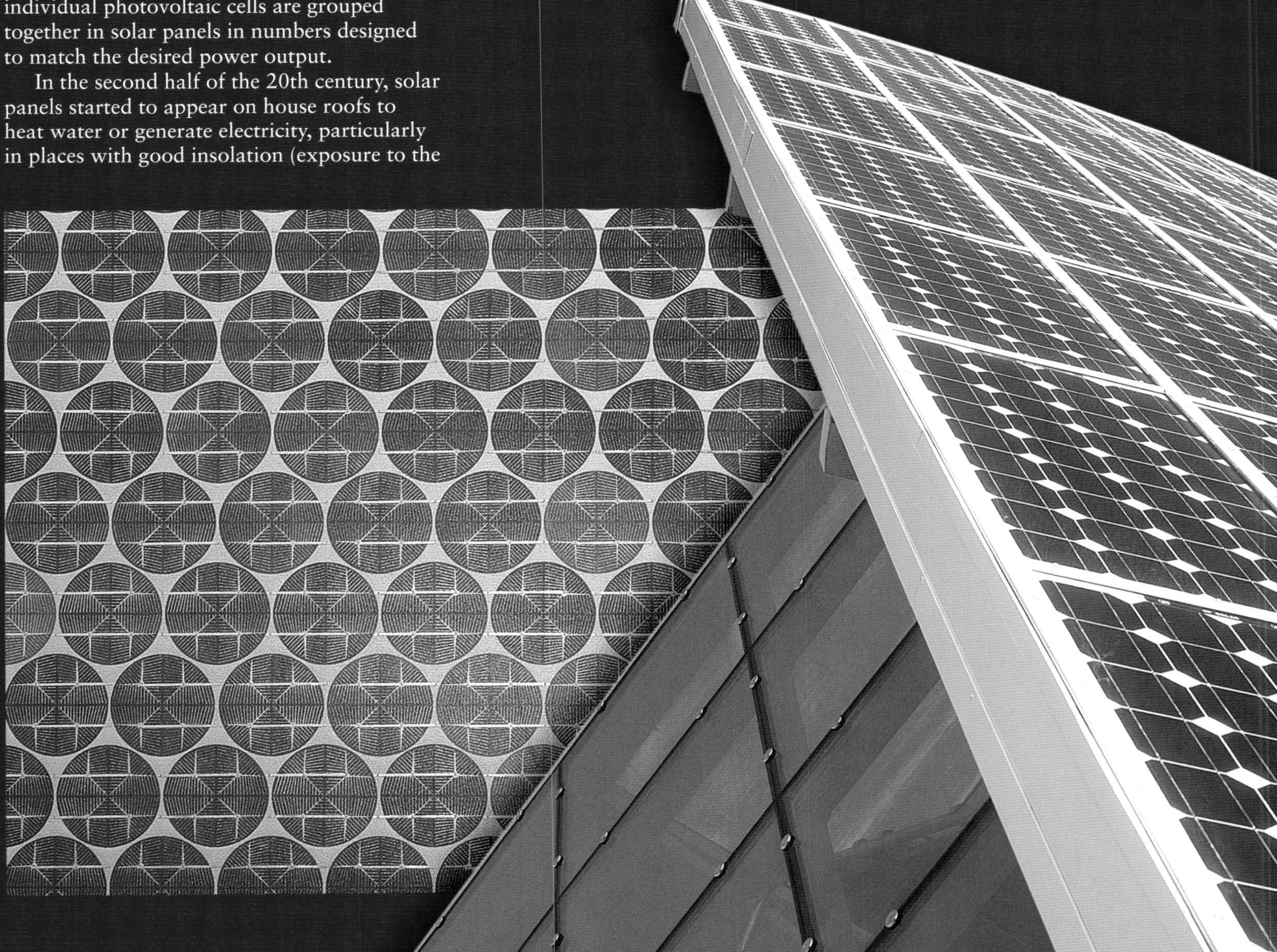

NEW GENERATIONS OF SOLAR PANELS

Silicon has the disadvantage of absorbing only a small amount of the light energy it receives, but cells incorporating narrow wafers of copper-iridium-selenium and cadmium telluride or other organic materials absorb light on all its wavelengths. Another technology involves converting low-energy photons into high-energy ones to maximise yields; an easily made ceramic filter can do the job. A third way of improving energy efficiency of solar lies in the development of plastic cells made from semi-conducting organic polymers. Power Plastic, as it is called, is cheap and supple, and can be used on a wide variety of different surfaces, from walls, windows and roofs to car bodywork and clothing. Nanotechnology also holds out promising prospects: paints and wall coatings incorporating photovoltaic nanotubes could provide new ways of capturing photons.

Solar array
These wave-shaped panels form part of the Andasol 1 power station, opened in 2009 near Grenada in Spain. It has a 50MW output – enough to power 45,000 homes.

has been done on boosting yields, which have improved six-fold over the past 30 years and which hopefully will go on increasing until solar electricity is at last competitive with other forms of power generation.

Another precondition if solar power is ever to fulfil its potential as an energy source is the need to feed the electricity it creates into established grids for distribution. The future here lies with high-voltage direct current (HVDC) transmission, which minimises energy loss and makes it possible to link areas with high sunlight, which are often lightly populated, with densely inhabited regions that have high energy consumption.

Still marginal

Limitless in extent and non-polluting, solar power has a great deal going for it, but the fact is that as an energy source considered on a global scale it remains marginal. In 1995 solar power accounted for just 0.2 per cent of the world's energy needs. By 2010 that figure had barely grown to just 0.3 per cent, still lagging far behind fossil fuels, of which petrol accounts for 31.5 per cent of energy consumption, coal 26.3 per cent and natural gas 19.5 per cent. Solar was also far outpaced by biomass (12 per cent, much of this figure

made up of the burning of wood), by hydroelectricity at 5.5 per cent, and nuclear power (5 per cent).

If it is ever to replace fossil fuels, which are heavy emitters of greenhouse gases, solar power will either have to become a lot less expensive or be given a helping hand by governments. In the USA financial incentives have already been put in place to encourage the use of solar and reduce the nation's dependence on oil, gas and coal. Britain has lagged behind on solar, largely as a result of its uncertain and variable insolation: in 2006 only 12.5 megawatts-peak (MWp) of photovoltaic capacity had been installed, equating to just 0.3 per cent of the European total for solar. Since then a feed-in tariff to encourage homeowners to install photovoltaic panels has been introduced, but this initiative is under review. Current projections suggest that even by 2020 just 0.5 per cent of the UK's electricity will be solar-generated.

At the start of 2010 the US firm SunEdison announced the construction of a gigantic photovoltaic power plant near Rovigo in northern Italy. The power station, which was completed in November 2010 and bought by the First Reserve Corporation, is the biggest solar plant yet built in Europe with an array extending over 850,000m^2 (210 acres). It went into production in December 2010 and is planned to provide enough power to supply electricity to 17,000 homes, thereby saving the release of an estimated 41,000 tonnes of carbon dioxide into the atmosphere. Whatever the current uncertainties, great things are expected of solar power in the future.

THE WORLD SOLAR CHALLENGE

Since 1987 the world's most futuristic solar-powered vehicles have gathered at two-year intervals to race 3,000km across the heart of Australia (above). The aim of the World Solar Challenge is to promote the use of non-polluting vehicles, which so far have not proved economically viable because of their dependence on direct sunlight and the limited power that this produces, given that there is not much room for solar panels on a road vehicle's roof. For the 2009 race, students at the Massachusetts Institute of Technology covered a three-wheeler they named 'Eleanor' in 6m^2 (65sq ft) of photovoltaic panels that between them produced 1,200W of electricity. Eleanor could travel all day long at 90km/h (55mph) – but only if the sun was shining.

Universal resource
Solar power is already helping to heat homes around the world, from the Mongolian steppes (below left) to Newton in Wales (below).

TWO FUTURISTIC PROJECTS

Solar islands: a Swiss company based in Neuchâtel has made the dream a reality by designing prototype floating power stations for the United Arab Emirates. These vast platforms, 5km across and 20m high, produce large amounts of clean energy at a reasonable cost of about 10-20p per kilowatt hour. Meanwhile, the Japanese are working on a solar space station. Planned to go into operation in 2030, the station will be placed into geostationary orbit outside the Earth's atmosphere, 36,000km (22,500 miles) above the planet's surface. There, the Sun's rays will fall on its 4km^2 (1.5 square miles) of photovoltaic panels without interruption, producing five or six times the amount of energy that could be achieved by a similar facility at ground level. Microwaves or a laser beam will be used to transmit the electric current back to Earth, where it will be captured by an immense parabolic reflector.

A SOLAR BOAT

Launched in Germany in March 2010, 'PlanetSolar' is a catamaran claimed by its makers to be the world's biggest solar-powered boat. Some 30m long by 16m wide, it uses no more energy than a motor scooter. In late 2010 'Planet Solar' set off to achieve the first circumnavigation of the globe powered solely by solar energy.

DIGITAL PHOTOGRAPHY – 1991

Shoot it and see

Initially, digital cameras were aimed at the mass market of amateur photographers looking for an easy way to take decent snapshots. They have since attained professional standards of quality, radically affecting the visual environment along the way.

In May 1991 Kodak, a leading presence in the camera and film market, presented its new Digital Camera System (DCS) at a press conference in New York. The system consisted of a processing and storage unit that was connected by cable to an image-capturing module fitted onto the body of a Nikon F3 SLR camera. The assembled device was the first professional-quality digital camera, doing away with the need for photographic film since the images were instantly transformed into digital data. The choice of a leading camera brand like Nikon as a partner meant that users could 'go digital' while retaining their existing lenses and accessories, not to mention their old way of taking photographs with film. The only problem was the cost of the DCS: between $20,000 and $25,000 depending on the model involved.

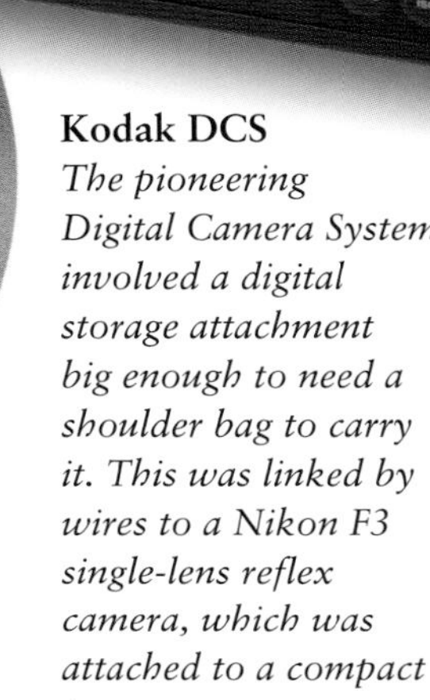

Kodak DCS
The pioneering Digital Camera System involved a digital storage attachment big enough to need a shoulder bag to carry it. This was linked by wires to a Nikon F3 single-lens reflex camera, which was attached to a compact image sensor.

Pixellated eye
Large-scale blow-ups of digital photographs reveal the individual pixels making up the image, which are usually invisible at normal size.

Trapping light

How could images be captured without the use of film? Willard S. Boyle and George E. Smith of Bell Laboratories worked out the answer to that questions in 1969 when they invented the charge-coupled device (CCD), which 40 years later won them the Nobel prize for physics. A thin layer of photoelectric material (they used silicon) transformed each photon (light particle) coming into contact with it into electric current. This was transferred instantly to an electronic device that converted it to a digital value. To capture a scene, the light intensity at each point was measured and the image reconstructed by juxtaposing all the points. A CCD thus consisted of a matrix of thousands of minuscule sensors, called photosites, each providing information for a given point or pixel (short for 'picture element') of the final image.

That was the case at least for black-and-white photographs, but silicon reacts indiscriminately to photons of different

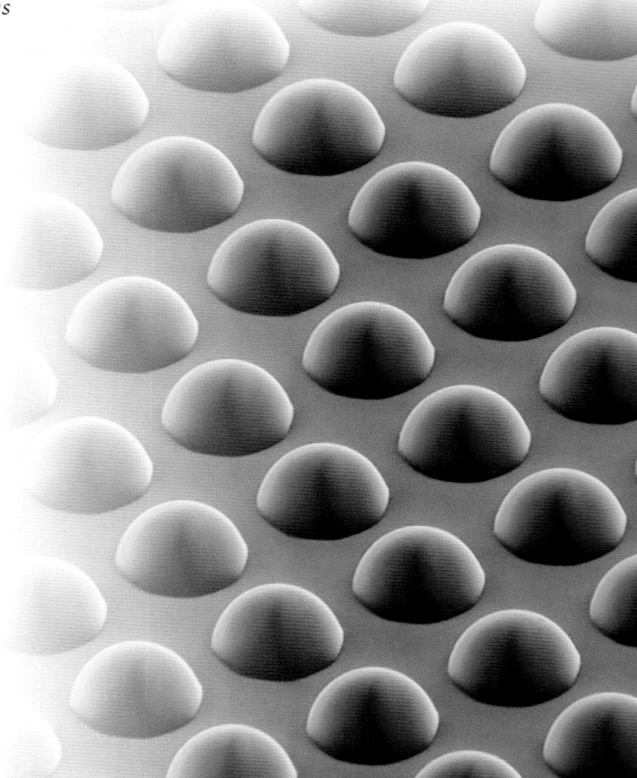

wavelengths and therefore to different colours, so for coloured images the light had to be filtered before it reached the photosites. Blue, green and red filters were used to reconstitute a spectrum of colours by what is known as an additive reproduction process. The fact that it takes three specialised photosites (in actual fact, four – a red, a blue and two separate greens, because of the peculiar sensitivities of the human eye) to colour a pixel meant that the degree of definition of the sensor was inevitably diminished. The first CCD image sensors, substantial in size, were developed for scientific imaging, in particular for use by astronomers, in the early 1970s.

In 1978 Steven Sasson, an electrical engineer working for Kodak, took out a patent for a digital camera. His device was still large – weighing 3.6kg, it was about the size of a toaster – but it already incorporated the basic principle of all subsequent devices, with a CCD image sensor taking the place of photographic film in a traditional camera. A television screen was needed to view the images, which were in black and white.

A mass-market product

Paradoxically, the early digital cameras were targeted at the mass market. Reduced-size image sensors were thought to provide photographs good enough for holiday snaps but not for professional photographers. Sony marketed the first digital camera in 1981; called the Mavica (short for Magnetic Video Camera), it could take 280,000-pixel images with the help of a CCD, but stored them in analogue form on floppy disks. It, too, produced images for viewing on a TV screen, although in its case they could also be transmitted down telephone lines. The Canon Ion RC-251 followed in 1985 and the Logitech Fotoman seven years later. Apple launched Quicktake, the first colour device, in 1994.

Later products stored the images digitally. In 1995 Casio introduced liquid-crystal displays allowing users to see what they were photographing on a screen at the back of the camera. CMOS image sensors, more sensitive than CCD, arrived in 2002, but were used primarily for reflex cameras (which allow the user to view the image to be shot through the lens itself), while devices intended for the lower end of the market continued to use CCD. As photosites became steadily smaller, the number of pixels an image sensor of any given size could register grew accordingly.

DCS IN ORBIT

On 24 November, 1991, the space shuttle *Atlantis* took off on one of its earlier missions. On board was a prototype Kodak Hawkeye II digital camera attached to a Nikon F3 body. The first digital photos taken in space appeared in newspapers soon afterwards, providing state-of-the-art publicity for Kodak's ground-breaking commercial model, using the same camera frame and sensor, which had been launched in New York just a few months earlier.

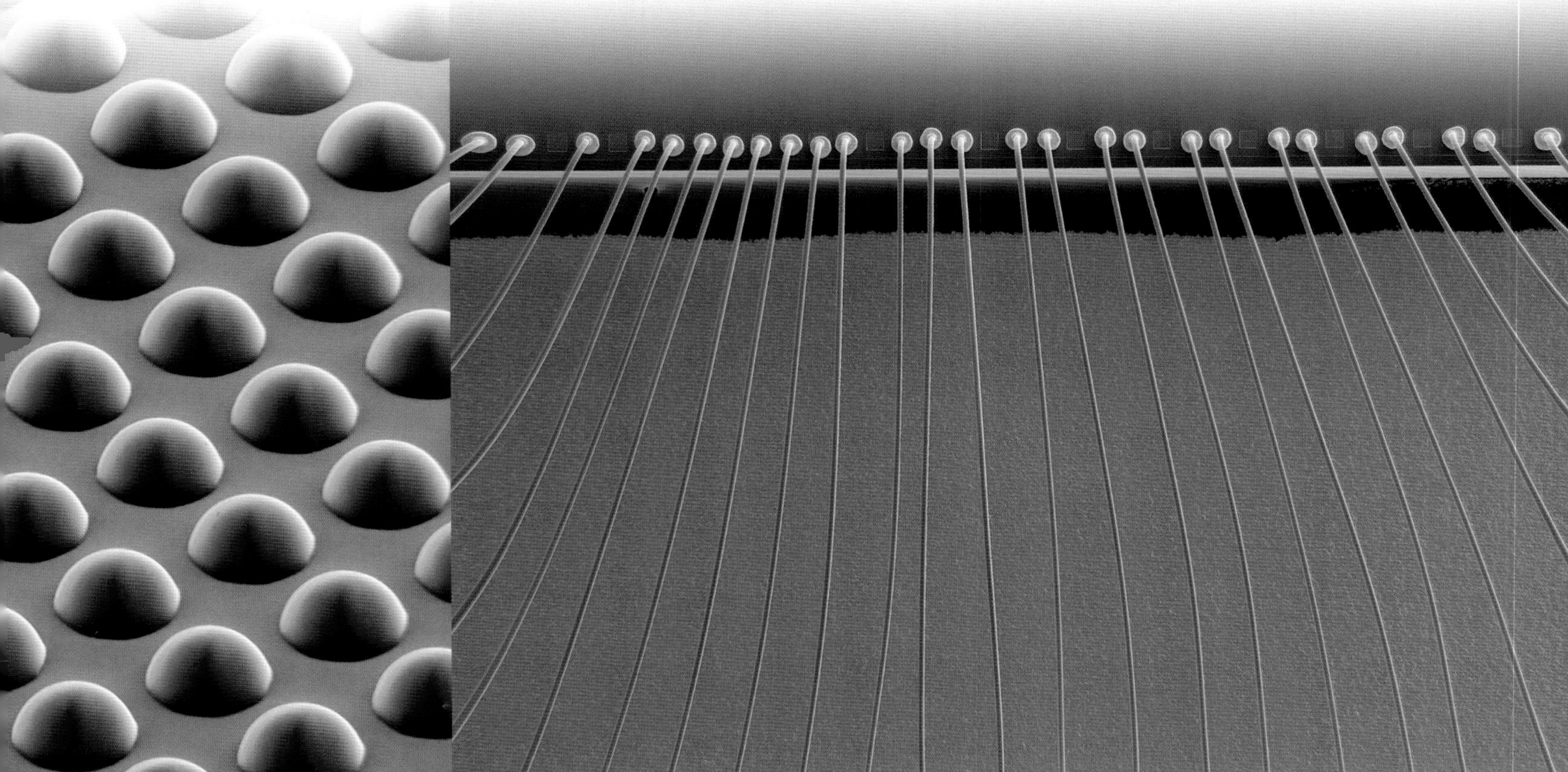

CCD technology
Photosites (below, left) are made up of one photodiode that receives light and another that transmits an electric charge. Each one corresponds to a single pixel in the finished image. Below: Electronic components of an image sensor.

Mass-market product
The Canon Ion RC-251 was launched in Europe in 1989. It was one of the first mass-market cameras not to use film.

A tool for professionals

For a long time professional photographers requiring top-quality equipment had no interest in digital devices. The story leading up to the launch of the DCS began with a first prototype in 1987. Kodak had developed a compact image sensor called the M1, with a capability of 1 million pixels; now it fixed this to the back of an existing camera, linking it with wires passing via the strap to a separate unit in a shoebox-sized black container that contained the battery, along with a hard disk for storing the images. The camera used in the prototype was a Canon F1, the Nikon F3's main competitor. Various prototypes followed, one of them designed for military use, employing increasingly powerful sensors and different storage systems that included memory modules as well as hard disks. Kodak modestly avoided calling the devices 'cameras', preferring to use the term 'imaging accessories', for the firm had no intention of killing off the market for traditional photographic equipment, which remained its bread and butter. Things began to change with the launch of the DCS in 1991. This had a liquid-crystal display on the storage unit and created images in black and white or colour with a resolution of 1.3 million pixels. Even so, the Nikon F3 to which it was attached remained a classic single-lens reflex (SLR) camera. Four years later Kodak created digital attachments for the Canon EOS range of SLRs (marketed as Kodak EOS–DCS), then for Swedish-made Hasselblads, the Rolls-Royces of studio equipment (the Kodak DCS 465).

The development of more powerful microprocessors soon did away with the need for the cumbersome storage unit. From 1998 on digital cameras became self-contained, starting with the Kodak DCS 500 series, which used a Canon body. Meanwhile, the batteries were also improving, an important point given the amount of electricity that digital cameras use. Soon afterwards, Kodak quit the market for professional-quality digital SLRs, leaving the field open to Nikon and Canon, who were better equipped to serve it. The following year Nikon brought out the D1 with 2.7 megapixel resolution, marking the real start of digital

NOSTALGIA FOR FILM

Some camera enthusiasts remain faithful to film, insisting that the quality of digital falls short of the earlier medium. In particular, they claim that it fails to pick up nuances in tones of grey and is over-sensitive to contrasts of light and shade. Others maintain that the use of filters and exploiting the special qualities of film in the development and printing process are essential parts of the photographer's art. But it is becoming increasingly difficult for people who do not have a darkroom to find laboratories capable of developing prints, particularly if there are any special requirements.

Inside a digital camera
This artist's impression shows the CCD image sensor behind the lens of a digital camera.

THE BULLET TIME EFFECT

In the late 19th century, the US-based English photographer Eadweard Muybridge used multiple cameras set up side by side to deconstruct motion, famously recording a horse's gallop. Digital photography, which permits cameras to be computer-controlled, has extended the possibilities of this approach. The 1990s saw the first animations obtained by successively releasing the shutters of a whole battery of still cameras. But it was *The Matrix* (above) that popularised the technique. The Chicago-born Wachowski brothers, who directed the film, set 120 cameras in an arc, using a computer to activate them one by one. Edited together, the images represented the scene as viewed from marginally different angles, creating an illusion of movement that no camera could in fact have captured. The brothers called the effect 'bullet time', a name that is now a Warner Bros registered trademark.

photography as a tool for photojournalists. Canon responded a year later with the D30, starting a technological rivalry that continues to this day, when resolutions of 21 megapixels have been attained. Once digital images had reached a satisfactory level of quality, the advantages of the system soon became obvious. Besides being easily saved, digital images could be transmitted instantly over the Internet and could easily be integrated into a production process that for newspapers and similar publications was by now entirely digital, from page layout to the printing.

During this time Kodak continued to produce digital add-ons for studio cameras designed for situations in which bulk was not an issue but quality reproduction was – for

On the job
Press photographers were won over to digital by the speed and convenience of being able to transmit shots downline to newsrooms for editing and printing.

Instant replay
A Tibetan family crowd around a compact digital camera to check out a group portrait.

ARE DIGITAL IMAGES EASY TO FAKE?

In a digital image each point of light has a numeric value made up of binary 0s and 1s. Computers can easily modify the numbers involved and so alter the resulting image – so much so that it has become almost impossible to detect fakes, and the boundary line between genuine photographs and synthetic images like this one (left) has become blurred. The process presents obvious dangers in news photography, but creative advertising agencies have leaped at the chance of creating striking surrealistic images, bringing a new aesthetic to posters and the pages of magazines.

fashion and advertising, for example, or for reproducing works of art. Resolutions of up to 50 million pixels were not unknown.

Digital developments for all

The public, meanwhile, had taken to the new devices with enthusiasm, to such an extent, in fact, that manufacturers were soon producing a range of models stretching from compacts suitable for taking holiday snapshots to SLRs designed for the most demanding amateur photographers. Advances in electronics added new features such as autofocus, digital zoom, red-eye removal, anti-blurring, on-screen editing, video capability and, most recently, smile detection mode. Users could fire off a seemingly limitless number of shots that could be played back instantly and deleted if not successful, then dispatched over the Internet or viewed on computer screens. As a result, digital imaging rapidly came to supplant traditional photography. By the year 2000 digital cameras were taking up the lion's share of the camera market. By 2006 film processing shops were closing down and even film manufacturers were dropping out of the market, leaving photography enthusiasts little choice but to switch to the new technology.

By no means everyone welcomed the change. Some people continued to lament the subtlety and tonal nuance of traditional cameras, insisting that digital images could never match the quality of film. That viewpoint

Personal record
A forest of mobiles are raised to capture the moment when Barack and Michelle Obama started off the dancing at an inaugural ball on 20 January, 2009, the day he was sworn in as US President.

PHONES THAT TAKE PHOTOS

In 2004 the general public got access to a new kind of camera: the mobile phone. Equipped with powerful sensors together with lenses that are adequate for most uses, the new devices were an immediate success – so much so that it has become difficult to find even an inexpensive mobile that does not take photos. Most devices can transmit the images to a third party via the MMS system as soon as they have been taken. In the early days of mobile telephony, people used to ask, 'Guess where I'm calling from?'; now it is often a matter of saying 'Look where I'm calling from!'.

Down in the deep
Thanks to efficient waterproofing, digital cameras can be used underwater, in some cases as much as 10m down.

fails to take into account the progress that digital technology has made, yet even now, when most professionals have switched to the new system, some hard-core enthusiasts still remain determinedly nostalgic for film.

Drowning in images

Easy-to-take photographs circulating freely in an increasingly developed rapid transmission network: that, in a nutshell, explains the extraordinary proliferation of images that surround us today. Freed from the costs associated with shooting on film, camera owners click away without restraint. New outlets have appeared for amateur efforts including blogs, online photo albums and the Multimedia Messaging Service (MMS), used to send photos over mobile phones. Employees of various services including police forces, insurance companies and estate agents now routinely use digital cameras to record information that previously would have required detailed notes. The Web also has a voracious appetite for images; some sites provide viewers with virtual tours of museums and similar attractions with the aid of montages of digital images. Medicine exploits the new technology to provide more informative pictures of the body – by highlighting diseased organs in different colours, for example. And scientists are making use of the ever more powerful image sensors, like the one installed on the Hubble Space Telescope, which has a resolution of 324 million pixels.

The Dyson bagless vacuum cleaner 1993

In 1978 the British designer and inventor James Dyson improved the air filter in a spray-finishing room that was regularly becoming blocked by dust particles. He did so by installing an industrial cyclonic separator that employed powerful centrifugal force to separate the particles from the surrounding air. From 1979 to 1984 he worked to apply the same principle to vacuum cleaners. The machine he developed sucked in air and spun it at great speed, relying on centrifugal force to throw dust and other debris to the side of the collection vessel, where it fell to the bottom ready for disposal, doing away with the need for dust bags. Meanwhile, the clean air was filtered and expelled. The DC01 was launched in Britain in 1993 and over the next three years 600,000 appliances were sold.

A MOST UNUSUAL FAN

In 2010 James Dyson launched the bladeless electric fan (right). It consists of a vertical ring fixed to a base containing a small electric motor. The airflow created by the motor is amplified by the ring, then projected into the room.

White-light LEDs 1993

The light-emitting diode or LED is an electronic component that gives off light when an electric current passes through it. A US engineer, Nick Holonyak Jnr, invented the first one to operate in the visible spectrum in 1962. For a long time it was thought that the chromatic range of the devices was limited to three colours – red, green and yellow – and their relatively high cost and low brightness restricted their use to fairy lights or nightlights. Blue LEDs were developed in 1971 by Jacques Pankove of RCA and were improved from 1990 on by Japanese-born Shuji Nakamura. In 1993 Nakamura used gallium nitride and indium gallium nitride semi-conductors to produce the first high-brightness blue-light LEDs. Used mostly in high-intensity car headlights, these were a major step forward toward the development of white-light diodes. White-light diodes use the three primary CRT (cathode-ray tube) colours of blue, green and red, added one to another and covered with a layer of phosphorus that absorbs part of the blue radiation, converting it to yellow: the mix of blue and yellow appears white to the human eye. White light opened up new possibilities for LED devices, from lighting for streets and homes to TV and computer screens.

Technology at the heart of sport

In the 1980s and 90s the world of sport showed an ever-increasing appetite for high-performance materials that could maximise the competitor's own prowess. Technology made inroads into every discipline, and star athletes became guinea-pigs for innovations that were later adapted for the mass market.

If ever there was a field in which engineers compete it is modern motor sport, as they seek to find some factor that will give their team the extra hundredth-of-a-second advantage that helps their driver take the top step on the podium. Formula One racing teams spend small fortunes acquiring the services of the best specialists in the very latest technology. Aluminium monocoque chassis, in vogue in the early 1980s, gave way to lighter, stronger carbon-composite structures. Michelin and Bridgestone proved the superiority of radial tyres. Turbocharged engines purred beneath bonnets, while the first computer-controlled active suspension systems appeared and wing design progressed to improve the road-holding capabilities of cars whose aerodynamic qualities were tested in wind tunnels.

Boats followed suit, although on smaller budgets. In 1980 the French yachtsman Eric Tabarly, on board the aluminium trimaran *Paul Ricard*, beat the record for the fastest

Aerodynamic design
For both downhill racing and giant slalom, skiers use poles that are curved to reduce air resistance. Downhill skis are 30 per cent longer than those used for slalom – the skier above was a giant slalom competitor – to provide increased stability at the high speeds achieved.

PHYSICAL FITNESS GOES HI-TECH

Feeling themselves short of exercise, a growing number of city-dwellers in the early 2000s took to shutting themselves up in gyms to work out on ever-smarter machines. Old-fashioned aerobics classes and body-building equipment were consigned to the dustbin of fitness history. The Nintendo Wii Fit video game and its attendant Balance Board took the development one step further. This by-product of the games industry transports users to a virtual gym to sweat it out under the instruction of an e-coach without even having to leave home.

Technical prowess
Gerhard Berger's McLaren Honda holds the road during a rainstorm in the 1991 Brazilian Grand Prix.

THE MAN WITH CARBON FIBRE LEGS

Thanks to modern prosthetic limbs, handicapped athletes are now achieving performances approaching those of the very best able-bodied athletes. South African sprinter Oscar Pistorius was born without fibulae in his lower legs, which had to be amputated below the knee as a result of the congenital bone malformation. Fitted with carbon-fibre limbs, he has run the 100 metres in 10.91 seconds, the 200 metres in 21.58 seconds and the 400 metres in 46.25 seconds.

crossing of the Atlantic in a sailing yacht that had been set by Charlie Barr back in 1905. Tabarly completed the journey in just ten days and five hours. Skippers, marine architects and naval designers were all soon eagerly exploiting the advantages of composite materials, notably carbon epoxy, which enabled them to construct the hull of a boat in one piece, doing away with the risk of leaks and corrosion. Winding gear, rigging, winches, autopilots and electronic systems that allow competitors to access GPS and check weather advice – all have been tested and improved on transatlantic races and circumnavigations before, in some cases, finding their way into production-line craft.

Top-of-the-range bicycles have become ultralight, with frames made in one piece out of Kevlar-reinforced carbon, a lenticular disc wheel at the rear and clipless pedals requiring special shoes. Wind-tunnel testing has helped to establish the optimal aerodynamic profile. As for mountain bikes, they now have telescopic suspension forks and disc brakes, innovations borrowed from motocross.

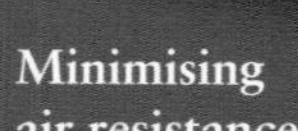

Minimising air resistance
US cycling legend Lance Armstrong photographed in the San Diego Wind Tunnel in California in 2008 (above). This unique facility allows cyclists to test out their aerodynamic profile.

Atlantic record-breaker
Yachtsman Eric Tabarly on the trimaran Paul Ricard *during his voyage across the Atlantic Ocean in 1980 (above).*

Power dressing
French swimmer Laura Manaudou competing at the 2004 Olympic Games. Her Arena Powerskin swimsuit was made of a material that eases the swimmer's passage through the water and absorbs 15 per cent less liquid than traditional fabrics. Polyurethane costumes were banned in 2010.

The business side of sport

New equipment is designed primarily for top athletes, who are viewed by manufacturers as ambassadors for their brand. Between 1985 and 1995 marketing budgets soared to pay for expensive sponsorship deals to boost brand image. The response from the general public was exactly what the manufacturers wanted, as the products promoted by sporting idols flew off the shelves of high-street stores. Anyone could now benefit from the enhanced performance initially available only to the few, perhaps by wearing a thermoregulating T-shirt using Outlast® textiles employing technology originally developed for NASA.

Yet for all the technological progress made, physical training remains the key to record-breaking sporting performance, calling on the efforts of doctors, kinesiotherapists, physical coaches, sophrologists, physiotherapists and dieticians. The reverse of the coin is that a number of champion athletes, seeking always to go higher and faster, have turned their backs on traditional ideals of sportsmanship by using performance-enhancing drugs. Fom steroids that boost speed and strength, to growth hormones that increase lean muscle mass, to drugs that combat fatigue, there is no shortage of substances to tempt professional athletes. Even amateurs sometimes ignore the health risks and take such stimulants.

Cutting-edge equipment

On ski slopes the late 1990s saw the arrival of so-called parabolic or 'shaped' skis, wider at the ends than in the centre. This new shape allows expert skiers to 'tailor' bends without slipsliding, leaving only the merest traces of their progress in the snow; amateurs, meanwhile, can make more turns without wearing themselves out. Adepts of freestyle and freeride perch on skis designed to provide optimal balance.

In tennis, traditional wooden racquets have been completely supplanted by synthetic fibre models that are more shock-absorbent and that speed up the pace of the ball off the strings. Fibreglass vaulting poles have gradually lost ground to carbon fibre, four times lighter but also more brittle.

Sportswear has also been evolving. Manufacturers of sports shoes have rivalled one another to introduce innovations ranging from the use of high-performance polymers to aerodynamic profiles and shaped soles designed to absorb impact. In clothing, new materials help to regulate body temperature, counteract sweating, support the muscles and limit rubbing. Through high-tech fabrics, full-body swimwear has becoming a second skin optimising movement through the water.

Well-heeled
Sports shoes have become ultralight – some weigh as little as 200g – and cater for different stride patterns and ground surfaces.

MANUFACTURING CHAMPIONS

Thanks to biotechnology, various natural tissues can now be used in cell therapy. In the world of sports, cartilage is the main focus of interest. The transplantation of chondrocytes (cells that produce cartilage) has become relatively common, even though it is banned in a number of countries. Gene doping (genetic modification to enhance performance) also seems to be on the increase. Technically speaking, for example, there is nothing to prevent trainers implanting genes associated with scar formation into an athlete's genome to increase the elasticity of tendons.

Science meets fiction

At first hearing, the concept of the mad scientist sounds like a contradiction in terms, for scientists should be the most rational people around. But the notion – now firmly fixed in the popular imagination – expresses a deep ambivalence in the public's attitude towards science: on the one hand pride in the achievements of the human intellect, on the other fear of the awesome powers that a small number of individuals have unleashed and of the unknown harm that they could do.

The struggle of good against evil
Spencer Tracey in the title role of Dr Jekyll and Mr Hyde *(above) filmed in 1941. In Robert Louis Stevenson's classic yarn, the mild-mannered scientist is haunted by an evil alter ego.*

The concept of the mad scientist entered the collective consciousness in 1817, with the publication of Mary Shelley's *Frankenstein*. In the novel, Victor Frankenstein seeks to create life by reanimating a corpse made up of body parts filched from exhumed cadavers. To do so he harnesses a new energy source which was being explored at the time the book was written: electricity. The monster that emerges as a result of these experiments spreads terror and panic in its path. In the 20th century Shelley's creation was brought to life for the cinema screen, reaching a huge audience.

In 1886 Robert Louis Stevenson published *The Strange Case of Dr Jekyll and Mr Hyde*. An honourable man, Jekyll suffers from a split personality disorder and is obsessed by unhealthy thoughts that find expression in the form of his alter ego, the criminally-inclined Edward Hyde. As a scientist, Jekyll develops a potion to separate the good from the bad within himself, but the bestial Hyde comes to dominate, the potion loses its effectiveness and the doctor becomes unable to re-assert his personality and regain his reason. Underlying the story is the 19th-century fascination with the unconscious mind and the phenomena of possession and spiritual mediums.

Thirst for power

It is only a small step from accepting the role that the unconscious plays in the human personality to seeking to manipulate it. That step was taken by Anton Mesmer (1734–1815), whose work on animal magnetism paved the way for modern hypnotism. Fiction writers soon endowed the technique with fearsome powers, as in Norbert Jacques' 1921 novel *Dr Mabuse the Gambler*, adapted for the cinema by Fritz Lang in the following year. A psychologist by training, Mabuse employs his talents as a hypnotist to criminal ends. His many successors in 20th-century fiction have included the demonic Septimus who enslaves Olrik in *The Yellow 'M'* (1956), and the protagonist of Kiyoshi Kurosawa's 1997 film

An evil genius
Dr Jonathan Septimus of the Psychiatric Institute is the villain of Edgar P. Jacobs' comic book The Yellow 'M', *published in 1956. This illustration (above) is © 2008 Blake and Mortimer/ Studio Jacobs n.a. (Dargaud-Limbard s.a.).*

A new twist
Andy Warhol produced Flesh for Frankenstein, *directed by his former assistant, Paul Morrissey. The film is an explicit adaptation of the familiar story with a woman as the monster*

The eyes have it
A poster for The Testament of Dr Mabuse *released in 1933. It was the second of three films made by Fritz Lang featuring the fictional criminal scientist and hypnotist.*

DO MAD SCIENTISTS REALLY EXIST?

André Marie Ampère, the father of electromagnetism after whom the standard unit of electric current is named, is often considered the model of the absent-minded professor. Eccentric to the point of putting his umbrella to bed one rainy night in 1836 while he slept on a doormat, he inspired the French cartoonist Christophe to create Cosinus, an archetypal image of the distracted savant whose adventures ran in comic-strip form from 1893 to 1899. The chemist Eugène Turpin took out a law suit for defamation against Jules Verne in 1896, recognising himself in Thomas Roch, the paranoid creator of a superweapon in Verne's novel *Facing the Flag*. The English author Norman Hunter based his Professor Branestawm books on the eccentric artist W. Heath Robinson, famed for his outlandish contraptions, who illustrated Hunter's original 1933 title *The Incredible Adventures of Professor Branestawm*. Some scientists have played up to the image: a famous photograph of Albert Einstein shows him sticking out his tongue at the camera, and he was quite happy to present himself to the public in the persona of the dishevelled eccentric.

THE TELLTALE SIGNS

'Naturally thin, very bald, with one of those beautifully polished scalps that recall the large end of an ostrich egg.' So Jules Verne described Palmyrin Rosette, the eccentric astronomer of his novel *Off on a Comet*. Like most mad scientist figures Palmyrin had a large head, to allow room for an apparently enormous brain, and a weak body, because eating came a long way down his list of priorities. Another incarnation of the mad scientist was Emmett 'Doc' Brown, the inventor played by Christopher Lloyd in the 1985 film *Back to the Future* (above). Brown was untidy and hirsute, with protruding eyes rolling in all directions as though to signify the non-stop activity going on behind them in his brain.

Only too aware of the powers his knowledge bestows upon him and wounded by the incomprehension of those around him, the mad scientist tends naturally to megalomania. Racked by fits of anger, he has an urge to shake his fist at the heavens, proclaiming himself master of the universe, perhaps to the accompaniment of a sardonic laugh in the manner of Dr Fatalis, sworn enemy of the Fantastic Four in the Marvel Comics strips. In practice, though, he cannot do without the help of lieutenants, disciples sworn to base dealings who are usually mentally simple and physically deformed, like the hunchbacked Igor of the Frankenstein films or the steel-toothed giant Jaws in the James Bond films *The Spy who Loved Me* and *Moonraker*. Finally, he lives in a remote house where he can carry out his satanic experiments far from prying eyes – a mansion from which unexpected bursts of light flash out on stormy nights . . .

Cure, whose hypnotic powers lead strangers to commit murders. Jules Verne created mad scientists capable of every type of monstrosity. Robur the Conqueror, the central character in *Clipper of the Clouds* (1886), creates a series of fantastic machines that give him mastery over the seas and skies and ends up by threatening to destroy all states that oppose his will.

All of these characters have one trait in common: if they are capable of the very worst actions, it is only because they started off with the potential to do great good. They combine technological prowess with scientific genius, so are able to put theory into practice, often using themselves as human guinea pigs. This can have unfortunate consequences, as in the 1958 film *The Fly*, re-made in 1986, when a teleportation experiment goes very badly wrong for the scientist. Transgression against nature is a staple element of such tales.

Test tubes and monstrous machines

The passage of time allowed writers and film-makers to endow mad scientists with an arsenal of research breakthroughs and technological advances. Electricity offered the illusion of limitless energy, providing the perfect background for diabolical activities. Dials and Tesla coils joined retorts borrowed from alchemy as essential props. In his 1927 silent film *Metropolis*, Fritz Lang invented a new screen model for the evil genius: the crazed Rotwang – with dishevelled hair and staring eyes, wearing a semi-military uniform – who creates a female robot in the depths of his laboratory. Rotwang's prosthetic right hand, symbolising humanity's erroneous pursuit of technological follies, would

Nuclear madness
Major T J 'King' Kong balances on a hydrogen bomb (right) in Stanley Kubrick's Dr Strangelove, or How I Learned to Stop Worrying and Love the Bomb *(1964). The title character in the film, played by Peter Sellers, is a former Nazi physicist re-employed as a scientific adviser to the US president.*

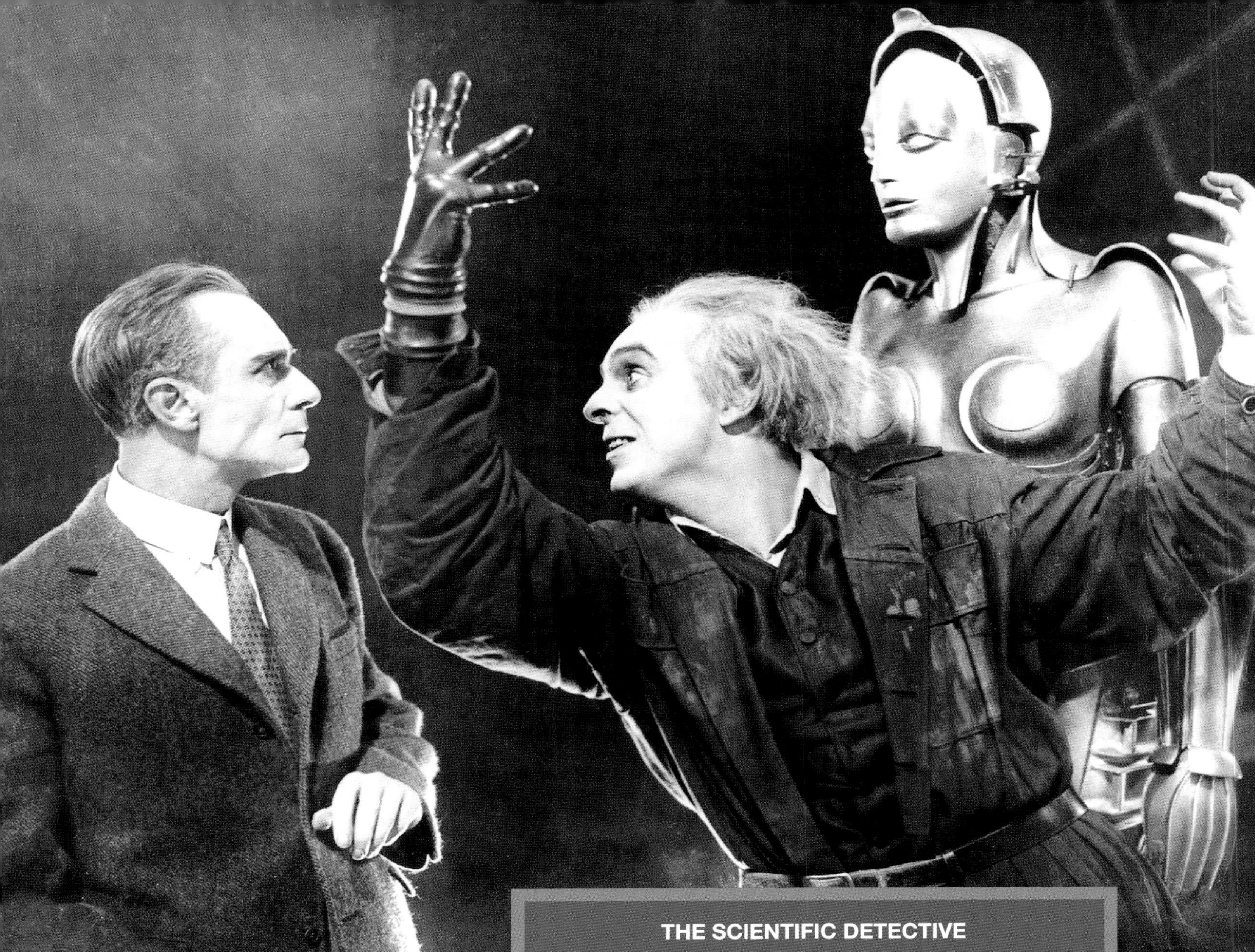

Machine maiden
Rotwang, the mad scientist in Fritz Lang's Metropolis, *confronts John Fredersen, ruler of the futuristic city, who looks nervously at Rotwang's robotic creation.*

inspire Dr Strangelove's reflex Hitler salute in Stanley Kubrick's film of 1964. Born of the fears engendered by the Cold War, *Dr Strangelove* ends with the outbreak of nuclear war as US bombs descend on an ICBM station named Laputa, the name given by Jonathan Swift to a flying island inhabited by crazed scientists in *Gulliver's Travels*.

Taking his inspiration from advances in surgery as well as from Darwinian theories of evolution, H G Wells created one of the most alarming physicians in literature in *The Island of Dr Moreau*. Moreau uses the scalpel and vivisection to shatter one of the last great taboos, the barrier between species, by seeking to give wild beasts human characteristics. Since

THE SCIENTIFIC DETECTIVE

The archetype of the scientific detective is Sherlock Holmes, created by Arthur Conan Doyle and memorably brought to life on screen by Basil Rathbone (below). Conan Doyle described his creation physically as thin with a piercing gaze and he endowed him with a love of smoking, cocaine and the violin. Holmes is solitary, antisocial and often misanthropic because he knows the evil of which people are capable. In the modern era, Canadian Kathy Reichs' female detective, Dr Temperance Daesee Brennan, is a forensic anthropologist who uses the most up to date methods to investigate human remains that are beyond the scope of usual evidence, as in cases of advanced decomposition or resulting from crimes such as arson. Like Holmes she is single (in her case divorced) and has struggled with addiction (to alcohol). In some respects the fictional scientific detective is a distant cousin of the mad scientist, but where the scientific spirit is driven by passion and imagination, cold logic is the guiding light of the detective.

Wolfman Jack
In the 2009 film X-Men Origins: Wolverine, *Hugh Jackman plays a superhero with claws that emerge in times of stress (above). He also has self-healing powers that help delay ageing.*

THE MAD SCIENTISTS' NEMESIS

Ian Fleming's James Bond is in many ways the antithesis of the mad scientist, particularly as portrayed on screen by Sean Connery, Roger Moore, Pierce Brosnan or Daniel Craig. Pleasure-loving, naturally elegant and an accomplished sportsman who displays true British phlegm, Bond represents the body in action. Even more than the sophisticated weapons and electronic gadgets he has at his disposal, it is Bond's muscles and general virility that see him through. Whatever the mission, Bond is a magnet for beautiful women, both friend and foe. The mad scientist he pursues is on the verge of destroying the world from a seemingly impregnable command headquarters on a radioactive island (*Dr No*), a space station (*Moonraker*) or in a command centre deep under ice (*Die Another Day*), but Bond can be relied upon to swim, ski or slide down ventilation shafts to penetrate the lair and emerge as the winner. The reassuring message in an age of increasing mechanisation is that human is still best.

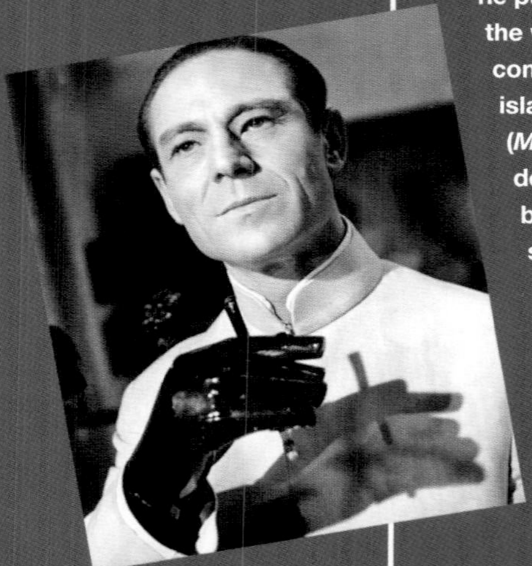

Face of evil genius
Joseph Wiseman as the eponymous villain in the 1962 film Dr. No.

Environmental catastrophe
Roland Emmerich's The Day after Tomorrow *(2004, below) imagines an episode of disastrous climate-change that brings a return of the ice age to much of the planet. But his scientists are heroes, not villains, struggling fruitlessly to avert the impending catastrophe.*

Wells's day, fresh hybridisation techniques such as genetic manipulation have further stimulated the imagination of novelists and scriptwriters. The comic-book superhero Wolverine, also featured in the 2002 film *X-Men* and its sequels, is the product of a military experiment gone wrong: provided with an indestructible skeleton, he is a beast trained to kill who struggles to hold on to his humanity. Philip K Dick wrote a series of novels on the subject of replicants, including *Do Androids Dream of Electric Sheep?*, the inspiration for Ridley Scott's film *Blade Runner*. Originally created to help humans to colonise Mars, Dick's androids are all but human in their biological functions, their propensity to feel and their weakness in the face of temptation.

Scientific dystopia
In Ridley Scott's 1982 film Blade Runner, *a futuristic Los Angeles is a monstrous megalopolis inhabited by robot replicants and afflicted by overpopulation, filth and omnipresent advertising.*

Rehabilitating scientists

As awareness grew of the damage that humankind has been inflicting on the planet, disaster movies and telefilms multiplied, covering subjects ranging from earthquakes (Mick Jackson's 1997 *Volcano*) and climate change accompanied variously by giant hailstones, tidal waves and a new Ice Age (*The Day After Tomorrow*) to the awakening of primordial creatures hidden in the ocean depths in the TV series *Surface*, released in 2005. In these fictional works scientists continue to be lonely figures, for no prophet is recognised in his own time or country, but they are no longer crazy or malevolent. Some, like the vulcanologist in Roger Donaldson's 1997 film *Dante's Peak*, are would-be saviour figures who use their expert knowledge to warn people of coming danger and to rescue what is left at the movie's end. In *The Day after Tomorrow* a palaeontologist who repeatedly warns of the threat of likely catastrophe sees a substantial part of Western civilisation disappear under ice. In his quest to reach New York and save his son, among others, he rediscovers the values that bind the human community together: courage, solidarity and love. In James Cameron's *Avatar* (2009), Dr Grace Augustine, head of a progamme liaising with the exoplanet Pandora, is the first person to revolt against the brutal exploitation of its inhabitants and to show, by her own death, the only possible way ahead: harmony with our own ecosystem.

All of these fictional forays reflect the fact that our attitude to scientists has changed. Blind optimism and irrational terror are increasingly being replaced by a pragmatism that expects scientists to pay fitting regard to the concerns of humanity and heed the words of the French satirist Rabelais written almost five centures ago: 'Science without a conscience is the soul's perdition.'

QUANTUM COMPUTERS – 1994

Putting particles to use to calculate

At the 35th Symposium on the Foundations of Computer Science, held in Los Alamitos, California, in October 1994, a mathematician from Bell Laboratories named Peter Shor created something of a sensation. He demonstrated that it might be possible to use quantum phenomena to create a calculating device more powerful than any ordinary computer.

In an address entitled 'Algorithms for Quantum Computation', Peter Shor combined computer language, complete with references to algorithms and bits, with the terminology of quantum physics, speaking of 'superposition' and the 'reduction of wave packets'. To the experts attending the forum, Shor's thinking added up to one thing: a revolution. He was showing how it might be possible, using the laws of quantum physics, to perform rapidly calculations that would take classic computers centuries to work out, no matter how powerful they might become at some future date.

Feynman's inspiration

Yet Shor's concept was not new. In 1982 the Nobel prize-winning American physicist Richard Feynman had sketched out the idea of a quantum computer. The basic notion involved putting the principle of the superposition of particles to use. For example, a particle in the realm of quantum physics can be in a state of both high and low energy at the same time. Feynman hoped to exploit this property: by using superposed particles as the base units for calculation (known as quantum bits, or more commonly qubits), an infinite number of calculations could in theory be carried out simultaneously, rather than sequentially as in classic computers.

Infinite possibilities

To see how this would work, suppose someone wants to find the whole-number divisors of the number 1517. A traditional computer would check out all the possibilities one by one, starting by dividing 1517 by 2. The result of that calculation would be 758.5, not a whole number, indicating that the figure 2 is not an exact divisor of 1517. Next it would try the

SHOR'S ALGORITHM

Shor's algorithm is based on the fact that the result of a quantum calculation is projected in the form of wave interference, which is to say as a figure in which luminous zones of different amplitudes alternate. Each amplitude corresponds to the probability of one particular result emerging at the time that the calculation is made. Shor demonstrated that it is possible to recognise the amplitude corresponding to the desired result, even when that result is not yet known. By manipulating the qubits several times, each time modifying some of the parameters of the system in order to gradually isolate the correct wave, it is possible to exclude all but the one sought, which can then be measured to get the required result.

QUANTUM LOGIC GATES

In a quantum computer, a logic gate is not a material device made up of a group of transistors, like the ANDs, ORs or NOTs in a traditional computer; instead, it is an interaction between qubits. Take for example a NOT gate: if a NOT gate is active (State 1), it transforms a binary 1 (the input) into a 0 and vice versa, while if it is inactive (State 0) the digits remain the same. In that way it can deliver four results: 0 or 1 (State 1) or 1 or 0 (State 0). But in quantum computing, by making two photons exhibiting different degrees of polarisation interact, it is possible to create a two-photon superposition. In the example given, one of the photons conveys a state of superposed polarisation (0,1) materialising the two possible states of the gate, while the other represents the input qubits (1,0). So the final state of the system is a superposition of all the possible results achieved by the traditional logic gate: 0,1,1,0.

Quantum lottery
In an artist's impression (above), dice rolling toward a black hole symbolise the subatomic universe postulated by quantum theory. The principle of indeterminacy spelled out by the physicists Werner Heisenberg and Erwin Schrödinger holds that it is never humanly possible to foresee exactly what is going to happen. Einstein challenged this view, maintaining that 'God does not throw dice'.

figure 3, giving 505.666, then 4, 5, 6 and so on. It would have to continue in this manner to 37 before it got a positive response, for 37 goes into 1517 exactly 41 times. So the classic computer would have to perform 37 separate operations to be able to give the response that 37 x 41 = 1517. If each operation took a second, the whole calculation would take 37 seconds in total.

In contrast, a quantum computer would simultaneously divide 1517 by 2, 3, 4 and all the other numbers up to 37, taking just 1 second to do the job. The time taken to do the multiple calculations would be the same regardless of the number of operations, be it 37 or 3,700. In theory, the machine that Feynman imagined was infinitely powerful.

From theory to reality
A quantum computer far left) developed by a team at the Technical University of Munich led by Professor Steffen Glaser. The researchers used magnetic resonance technology to superpose five qubits.

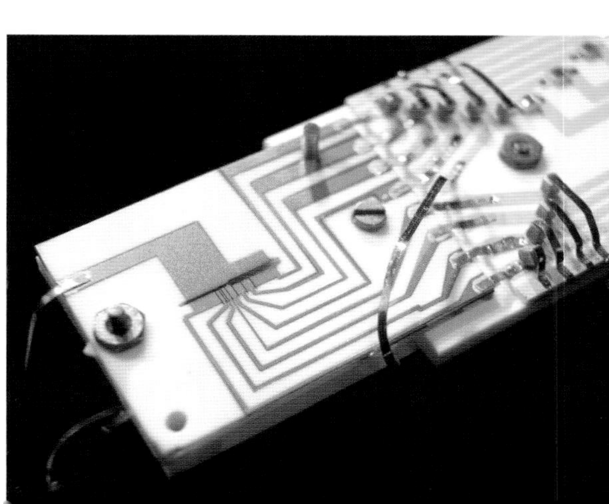

Breaking new ground
A device (right) used by John Jost and a team at the US National Institute of Standards and Technology to show that a quantum interaction also presents itself as a mechanical phenomenon.

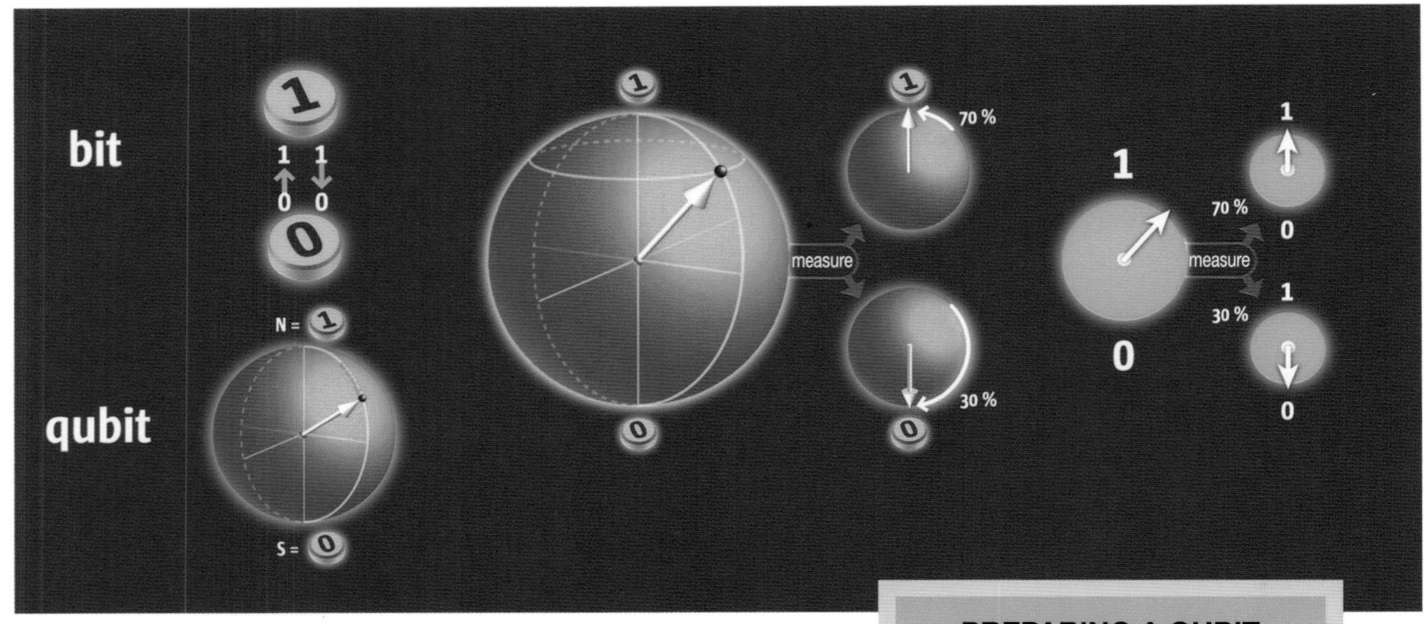

The building blocks of quantum calculations
The fundamental unit of quantum computing is the qubit. Unlike the binary bits of traditional computers, which always have a value of either 0 or 1, qubits can have an infinite number of values. For purposes of illustration, the position of the qubit represented above is shown by an arrow indicating its location on the surface of a sphere. To quantify its state, it would be classed as 1 if it was located at the top end of the sphere and 0 if it was at the bottom. The position of the arrow here indicates that there is a 70 per cent chance of the qubit having a value of 1 and a 30 per cent chance of its value being 0, as indicated diagramatically to the right. The use of spheres and arrows is of course a simplification, for in reality a qubit can, thanks to the phenomenon of superposition, occupy multiple positions at one and the same time. In effect, the arrow could be pointing simultaneously to almost any point on the sphere's surface.

PREPARING A QUBIT

To produce a qubit, researchers make use of the polarisation of light as expressed through the orientation of its magnetic field, a phenomenon that is also exploited in 3D films. Light can be polarised in several directions, for example, upward to the left. But the laws of quantum physics make it possible to prepare isolated photons whose direction of polarisation is at one and the same time upward *and* to the left – a phenomenon that equates in computer terms to a combination of the digital binary numbers 0 and 1.

CHALLENGING THE NOTION OF IDENTITY

Quantum mechanics postulates that particles, atoms or electrons can change identity depending on the viewpoint from which they are observed. They can also have different attributes, or even be in more than one place, at the same time.

Shor's breakthough

In practice, though, there was a problem. The moment that a result was reached, be it 758.5, 505.666 or whatever, it risked instantly being lost, for only one response could be accessed at a time – and that not necessarily the right one. Shor's breakthrough in 1994 lay in demonstrating a way of extracting the desired result by way of a few supplementary manipulations that put a limit to the infinite capacity of quantum computation while still allowing it to achieve results well beyond anything that a traditional computer could manage. His discovery inspired a fever of excitement in the information technology community, and hundreds of millions of dollars have subsequently been invested in seeking to explore this new field of research.

The first results

The high level of interest is easily explained, for if such a computer could be built, it would instantly compromise the security of all other existing computer networks. In effect, the task of finding divisors for huge numbers underlies the encryption of all data that circulates in digital form – money transfers, electronic mail and the rest.

Beyond that, the unimaginable power of a quantum computer would affect every aspect of information technology. In particular, such a computer would represent a breakthough in the handling of sequential-logic problems, making it possible to find in an instant the best solution out of a whole multitude of options. So a research engine would no longer have to visit every site on the Web individually to index key words; it could achieve the same result at a single stroke. In 1998, researchers at IBM announced the start of that breakthrough with the development of the first two-qubit quantum computer. But doubts persisted.

Fast but fragile

In such systems any outside influence, from physical contact to radiation, can destabilise the quantum superposition, destroying the calculation even as it is being carried out. Worse still, the more qubits involved, the more fragile the operation becomes. One expert, the Israeli-British physicist David Deutsch, has estimated that 300 qubits would have to interact to produce a device that could realistically compete with a top-of-the-range traditional computer, and nothing approaching that has so far been achieved. In 2001 IBM researchers managed to manipulate seven qubits in a state of superposition for a few minutes by holding chloroform molecules in suspension with the aid of nuclear magnetic resonance technology. Five years later, 12 qubits were superposed in similar fashion.

An endless single-sided ribbon
This sculpture (right) by the Swiss artist Max Bill, now on display at the Pompidou Centre in Paris, takes its inspiration from the Möbius strip. A continuous ring with a twist in it, the shape was first described in 1858 by the German mathematician August Möbius. It has the peculiarity of having only a single side – a neat illustration of the sort of tricks quantum thinking can play on conventional logic.

QUANTUM CALCULATION

In a quantum calculation, each logic gate (or qubit) receives a system of qubits already superposed by the previous one, to which it in turn superposes its own qubit. If the first gate has superposed the results of a 2-qubit calculation, providing four results, the next adds an extra qubit, providing eight results, and so on. By the time the *n*th operation has taken place, the system contains the two original results to the power of *n*. In short, it is as if, with each successive operation, the quantum computer doubles the possible number of combinations available to a traditional binaray computer.

Future hybrids

Today IT specialists are seeking to develop solid nanocomponents incorporating quantum dots, superconductors and other features within which qubits could effectively interact. In 2009 researchers at Yale University produced a 2-qubit solid processing unit. Perhaps not surprisingly, the excitement that Shor's breakthrough generated initially has tailed off somewhat as scientists came to realise that the inherent instability of quantum phenomena might make it impossible to ever develop a true quantum computer. Even so, the field is still attracting a great deal of attention, for the future of computing may lie in hybrid systems employing a mixture of traditional and quantum elements.

Seeking the Bose-Einstein condensate
A researcher (above left) uses a laser to chill gas atoms to a temperature close to absolute zero. At that point the loss of thermal energy slows the atoms down to such an extent that they all exhibit the same quantum state and become indistinguishable from one another. Albert Einstein predicted this phenomenon in 1924, basing his views on work done by the Indian physicist Satyendra Nath Bose.

Stirred, not shaken
Agitated by two laser beams revolving around one another, a cloud of atoms is caught in a vortex that facilitates the formation of Bose–Einstein condensates (left).

VIDEO ART

Technology in the service of art

Since the 1960s the boundaries between different branches of the arts have been lowered. New imaging tools such as video, camcorders, digital television and computer graphics have opened fresh avenues for artistic creation.

In the USA at the start of the 1960s, Robert Rauschenburg began introducing objects – stuffed birds, a ladder, radios – into his 'combine paintings', while Tom Wesselman incorporated a turned-on television set into a still life. Meanwhile, Andy Warhol was videotaping everything that happened at his Factory, an avante-garde hothouse for various kinds of experimental artistic activity. In Europe a group of artists launched the Fluxus movement (which also had New York connections) in a spirit of playful contestation. Inspired by improvised 'happenings', the Fluxus artists were interested in ephemeral art, creating environments and organising concerts featuring pioneers of experimental music such as John Cage and La Monte Young.

One artist associated with the group, the Korean-born American Nam June Paik, began in 1962 to experiment with cathode-ray tubes from black-and-white televisions, using a magnet to distort the images; he achieved similar effects by manipulating the transistors of early colour sets. He also used a Sony Portapak, the first portable video camera able

Closed-circuit art *Bruce Nauman's* Mapping the studio II with color shift, flip, flop & flip/flop (fat chance John Cage), *made in 2001 (below), involved filming his empty studio for an hour at a time at night, building up a total of 42 hours of material. He used a video camera with infrared capability, set up in different locations and left running. The result was a series of static, hour-long films recalling footage from video surveillance cameras.*

CELEBRATING ELECTRONICS

In 1989 the Paris Museum of Modern Art marked the 200th anniversary of the French Revolution with a video installation by Nam June Paik. The artist took the commission to heart: 'The Revolution is not just a combat but also a trigger for technological development.' He built five robots out of old television sets with colour monitors showing computer images (above). Voltaire appeared surrounded by other individuals who had influenced the Revolution, including the feminist playwright Olympe de Couges. In 2010-11 Tate Liverpool staged the first major retrospective following the artist's death in 2006. Among the works shown were 'Video Fish' (1979-92), which sets nature against the manmade and features live aquarium fish, and the groundbreaking satellite video 'Good Morning Mr Orwell' made in 1984.

to record sound, to film happenings, concerts and early examples of performance art. In 1965 he filmed the cellist Charlotte Moorman performing John Cage's *26' 1.1499 for a String Player*, then later, in the 1970s, the work of the choreographer Merce Cunningham. Today, much of video art output remains closely linked to music, dance and stagecraft.

Different directions

Video art is in fact an umbrella term covering a range of activities, sometimes in combination with one another. While some artists express themselves through installations, others use the video screen merely as a way of projecting standard or experimental video tapes. Following the example of Nam June Paik or the American photographer Peter Campus, they use a range of apparatus to create forms, rhythms and colours. They may exploit the artistic possibilities of feedback, distortion or permutations of colour. They may also return the image to its point of origin by placing the camera in front of the monitor.

Some video artists, like Chantal Akerman, Jean-Luc Godard or Chris Marker, have a background in cinema. Others express themselves through the medium of television, like Britain's David Hall, who trained as a sculptor then went on to use multi-channel television as an artistic medium. In 1971 ten of his works, all commissioned by the Scottish Arts Council for the Edinburgh Festival, were transmitted unannounced over a ten-day period by Scottish Television. The first artist interventions on British television, they are regarded as a formative moment in video art.

In the USA the New York station Channel 13 opened its airwaves to artists. Some were painters like John Baldessari, who made videos and experimental films before returning to his artistic roots, enriching his canvases with photographs, collages and images from films. Vito Acconci wrote poems whose conceptual approach led him first toward the visual arts and then to a reflection on the place of his own body and of the spectator in performances. Bill Viola created experimental tapes inspired by his researches in electronic music, before producing monumental installations accompanied by deafening soundtracks.

Digital dance
Merce Cunningham's Biped, *created in 1999, was one of the first choreographic works to employ computer graphics and digital imaging.*

Moving to the Internet

The installation of a video work brings together the objects involved in recording and broadcasting that work: video cameras, tape recorders, monitors, projectors, microphones and loudspeakers. It requires participation from the spectator, who has to take up a position from which to experience the work. While Nam June Paik used families of robots to create video sculptures, in the USA Bruce Nauman involved spectators by making them edge down 'video corridors' to contemplate their own image on a screen, caught by a closed-circuit camera. Dara Birnbaum was one of the first people to create 'video walls'

THE ABE-PAIK SYNTHESISER

Developed in 1964 by Nam June Paik and the Japanese engineer Shuya Abe, this apparatus made it possible to edit images from seven cameras at the same time and to produce coloured forms from black-and-white images. It could also be used to modify and distort colours and contours and produce sounds. Many video artists made use of it, while others including Eric Siegel, Bill Etra and Steve Rutt, and Stephen Beck have come up with similar devices of their own.

VIDEO ART AND BODY ART

Using one's own body as a means of expression is an intimate and highly personal form of art that can lend itself easily to narcissistic rituals and transformations – sometimes even mutilations – as well as to feminist statements. Women video artists have taken a particular interest in body art. In the 1970s Italy's Gina Pane explored the concept of pain by slashing her own flesh in the course of video performances. The French artist Orlan challenged Western notions of beauty by employing plastic surgery to remodel her face under the camera's eye. Perhaps the most disturbing work of all was *Foreign Body* (1994) by the Lebanon-born Palestinian Mona Hatoum, who used an endoscopic camera to explore her own bodily orifices.

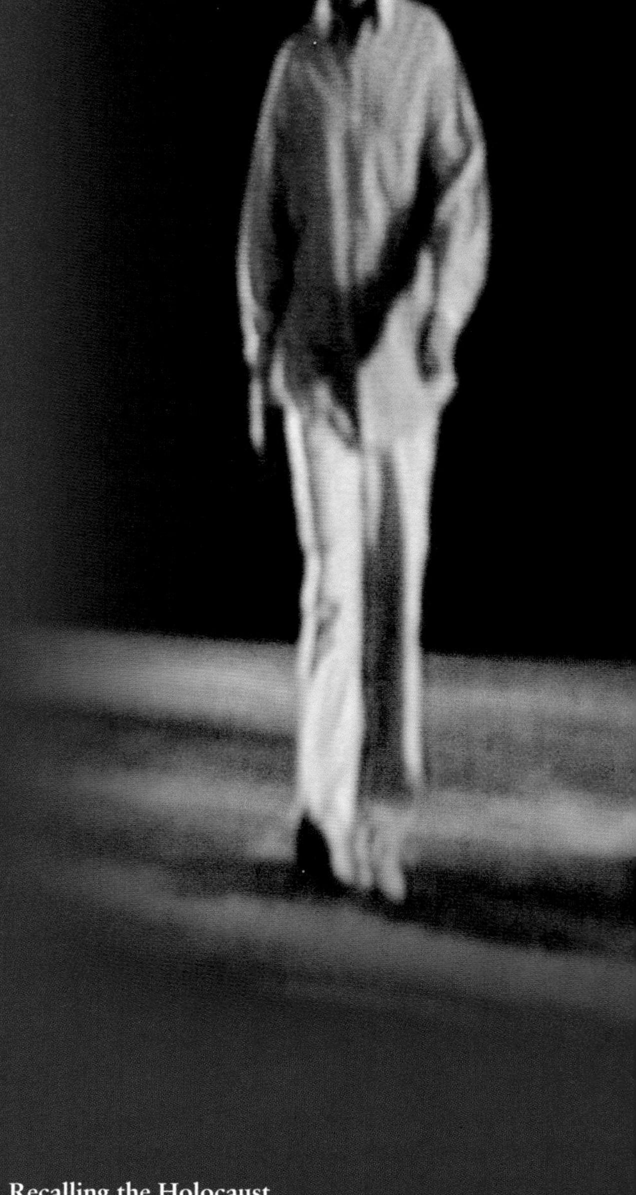

Talking heads
Kutlug Ataman's installation Küba *was staged at the former Sorting Office in London's New Oxford Street in March 2005. The Turkish artist filmed residents of Küba, a squatter settlement in Istanbul, speaking straight to camera. His aim was to get people to reveal their personalities through their comments.*

displaying either multiple versions of a single image or else different images on a number of different screens. These were no longer necessarily cathode-ray devices, thanks to the arrival first of video projectors that played images on a screen, as in the cinema, and then of LCD and plasma displays. From the 1990s on, video art has often been exhibited in a 'black box' setting, a sort of sanctuary cut off from the light-filled galleries around it where traditional art is shown. If the black boxes tended to conceal the technology involved, Fabrice Hybert's installation at the 1997 Venice Biennale flaunted it, re-creating a television studio complete with cameras, monitors, production control room and all the indispensable audio equipment. The technology became the subject of the work.

In the 1980s and 90s, video artists began to explore the infinite possibilities that opened up with the dawning of the digital age. Other

Recalling the Holocaust
Esther Shalev-Gerz's installation Between Listening and Telling: Last Witnesses, Auschwitz 1945–2005 *(below) has been shown in cities around the world. It featured Holocaust survivors describing their experiences in the death camp.*

innovations such as touch screens helped to enhance audience participation by giving the spectator the ability to influence the way in which a work developed. Moving out of museums and galleries altogether, it found a new home on the Web. It may well be that sites such as YouTube and Dailymotion, which bring together films, amateur videos and simple visual jokes as well as more experimental works, are currently doing the most to carry to the biggest possible audience an art form that has now come to maturity.

Personal drama
Bill Viola's video installation The Crossing *(1996) showed slow-motion footage on back-to-back screens of the artist walking towards the spectator. When he finally stopped, on one screen he was consumed by flames from the feet up, while on the other he was slowly submerged by a stream of water poured onto his head.*

VIDEO ART'S NEW FRONTIERS

Video art only reached Russia after the collapse of communism, and it was also a late arrival in Eastern Europe, the Middle East and China. For artists in those countries, political and artistic preoccupations were often linked, as in the Hungarian Péter Forgács' 1988 documentary about daily life under Stalin, *Private Hungary: The Bartos Family*.
In China in 1991, Shi Jian and Chen Jue explored the events of 1989 in Tienanmen Square. Living in exile in the USA, Shirin Neshat combined music and video to denounce relations between the sexes in her native Iran; in her 1998 installation *Turbulent*, a singer interprets a Persian ballad while a woman emits unintelligible sounds, as though muzzled.

Street art
Canadian artist Rafael Lozano-Hemmer's Under Scan *was projected onto the pavement of London's Trafalgar Square in 2008 (below). When the shadows of passers-by touched its images of sleeping figures, they appeared to wake up and react.*

DVDs

1995

In 1995 a global consortium of leading electronics firms, comprising Philips, Sony, Hitachi, JVC, Matsushita, Mitsubishi, Pioneer, Thomson, Time Warner and Toshiba, prepared to launch DVDs as the successor to compact discs (CDs). The new products looked very similar to CDs and worked in the same way. What was different about them was their far greater storage capacity – at least 4.7GB, enough to carry 135 minutes of video film. That was seven times as much as CDs, which could only manage 650MB, equivalent to 74 minutes of music. The lasers used to record DVDs worked on a shorter wavelength, enabling them to concentrate more information in the available space. The new medium rang the death knell for VHS cassettes, and sales had already overtaken CDs by the turn of the century.

There are different kinds of DVD, depending on whether they are single-sided or double-sided and employ one or two layers. A single-sided single-layer DVD can store 4.7GB of data, while a double-sided, double-layer disc supports almost 17GB, equivalent to eight hours of video programming.

Sights and sounds
The information contained on a DVD, whether images or sounds, is carried on a spiral track marked by bumps and pits. The differing depths between the hollows (marked in blue below) and the flat surface (shown in white) generate a digital signal, either 0 or 1, which codes the information. The image below is magnified 1,500 times.

A versatile medium

DVDs owe their success to more than just their storage capacity. The quality of the sound and pictures they delivered heralded the age of digital leisure. They stimulated the creativity of producers, gave a new lease of life to classic films, and offered viewers a mass of new applications, from freeze-frame capability and scene selection to bonus features including interviews and production information. The little discs brought the cinema and live music into the home. Their increased storage capacity also made them suitable media for educational programmes, video games and camcorder recordings. But the multiplicity of uses has also had a downside; the accumulation of different disc-reading systems has done little to help with compatibility between devices.

COMPRESSING DATA

To cram so much information onto DVDs, different algorithms are used to compress the data, and this can influence the picture quality of the video concerned. The ones most often used employ either the MPEG-2 standard, set by the international Moving Pictures Expert Group, or else the Div-X, based on the MPEG-4 standard, for extra-large video files.

Blue lasers 1995

Coloured lasers held no secrets for the Japanese researcher Shuji Nakamura, who in 1993 developed the first blue-light laser, using a gallium nitride diode. His invention would have a dramatic effect on the data storage techniques employed for DVDs, but also had important implications for energy conservation, winning him Finland's Millennium Technology Prize in 2006, among other honours. Major laboratories were soon competing to master this revolutionary new light source. Blue lasers have a wavelength of 405 nanometres, as compared with the 635nm of orange lasers employed for DVDs and the 780nm of the red lasers used with CDs, so the blue beam allows for more data storage. The first mass-market devices employing blue lasers appeared in 1997, following large-scale investment by the Japanese industrial giants.

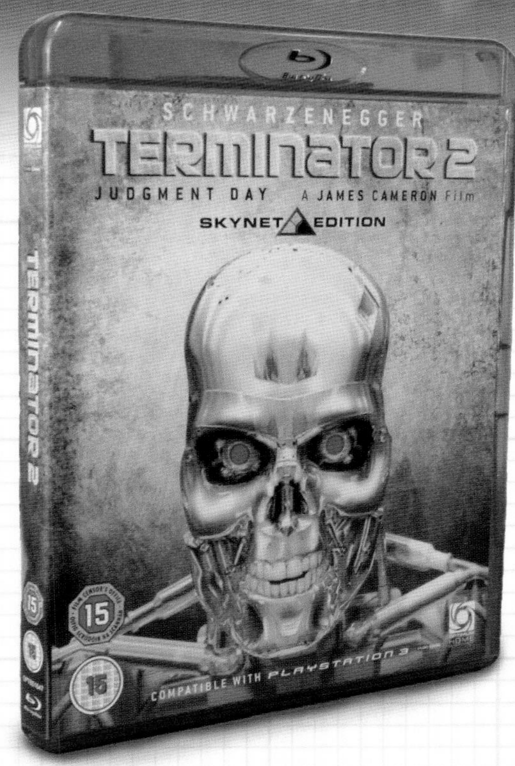

Updating a classic
In 2009 the long awaited Blu-ray (Skynet) edition of James Cameron's 1991 movie Terminator 2: Judgment Day *was released. Fans were now able to see and hear multiple versions of the movie in explosive high-definition. The disc had more than eight hours of interactive Blu-ray content including over 140 minutes of behind the scenes videos, storyboard-scripts, commentaries, quizzes and games.*

Ever more storage capacity

But even before it established itself, the technology became the focus of a growing rivalry. Two camps formed over the discs, which in practice still looked like DVDs despite holding more than five times as much data. Sony backed the Blu-ray format, while Toshiba championed its own HD-DVD standard. Hostilities came to an end in 2008, when leading US companies, headed by Time-Warner, opted for Blu-ray, putting an end to a period when consumers had to choose one or the other without knowing which would survive. As for traditional DVDs, they continued to increase sales and still have a secure future. Even so, Blu-ray is beginning to take off: sales in the UK reached £15 million in 2010-11, ten times the previous year's figure. Market analysts expect a further spurt with the arrival of 3D Blu-ray discs, making it possible to view films at home in three dimensions.

BLU-RAY DISCS

Like DVDs, Blu-ray discs come in different formats. BD-ROMs are read-only. BD-Rs can be recorded but only once as the material is permanently stored on the disc, while BD-REs can be recorded and wiped repeatedly. A single-layer Blu-ray disc has a 25GB capacity, while double-layer versions can store up to 50GB of data.

A question of identity

For a long time, biometric techniques were limited to identifying fingerprints, but they have come a long way since the 1980s. A range of factors can now be used to identify individuals, from appearance and behaviour to biology. Many new applications are being developed.

Dulles International Airport, Washington, November 2007. A queue lines up between the barriers. One by one, the passengers present their passports to the immigration officer, place all ten fingers on a scanner screen, then turn toward a digital camera. This first step toward enrolling the biometric data of foreign nationals was taken in the USA in the name of the war against terror.

The airport arrival procedure is just one example among many of the increasing use of biometric techniques. Based on the analysis of physiological or behavioural characteristics considered unique to each individual, they serve to establish people's identities. They are used for two main types of application: identification, whether by police or the law courts for protection against criminal or terrorist acts, and authentication, authorising access to sensitive or secure sites.

Stand and be recognised
A passenger at John F. Kennedy International Airport in New York has his thumbprint scanned while a digital camera takes his picture.

Fingerprints point the way

The idea itself dates back at least to the 1870s, when the Parisian police began to take measurements of different body parts and noted down distinctive features, accompanied by photographs, to help identify criminals. Nicknamed *bertillonage* after its creator Alphonse Bertillon, this anthropometric system was adopted across France in 1887 and also came to be used in other countries. But it proved insufficiently reliable and by the turn of the 20th century fingerprinting had replaced bertillonage as the surest means of identifying criminals.

The first automated procedures

Biometrics as we know it today is based on automated recognition technologies. In 1975 the FBI financed the development of sensors able to locate fingerprints from files by comparing distinctive features. The progress of analytical algorithms subsequently made it possible to pre-select close matches, speeding up the process. In 1994 the Integrated Automated Fingerprint Identification System (IAFIS) won investigators precious time by bringing together all the available databases. The procedure employed was reliable enough, for the chances of two people sharing the same prints is of an order of 10^{-24}, and it was also easy to use, but it was not foolproof. For instance, in some cases no fingerprints were found at the crime scene, or false prints moulded in latex could be left deliberately to confuse investigators. So it became necessary to develop other, supplementary technologies.

AUTOMATING AIRPORT SECURITY

Airports worldwide have begun testing biometric security. In Europe voluntary systems have been adopted, such as the French system of fingerprint scanners for passengers from the Schengen area countries. Iris recognition (see page 124) is also being widely introduced. In the future, it might be ear recognition. Researchers at Southampton University have discovered that each person's ears have a unique shape and have created a system to scan them.

Data retriever
The FBI maintains a vast forensic database that in 2002 already had some 300 million fingerprints on file. To access the information, the agency employs six automatic servers. A robotic arm (at top right in the photo) locates, retrieves and replaces the required data.

BIOMETRIC PASSPORTS

All passports issued in the UK are now biometric, containing detailed information about the holder's face – for example, the relative distances between eyes, nose and ears – on a machine-readable computer chip. The addition of fingerprints is also under consideration. Other European countries have gone further: since 2009, for example, French passports (right) have included two fingerprints.

Print pioneer
The promotion of fingerprints for criminal detection owes much to Henry Faulds, a Scottish scientist and medical missionary who worked in India and Japan. His drawings above, dating from 1905, show different identifying patterns.

Recognising faces

After an inconclusive trial in 1974, the first operational device for recognising palm prints was patented in 1985. It, too, was simple to use but it remained unreliable, better suited to authentication than identification. Since the year 2000, systems using infrared images of the palm of the hand or fingers have come into use. Based on recognition of traces of veins below the skin, the PalmSecure system, put on the market by the Japanese firm Fujitsu in 2005, is used to control access to Japanese banks and to at least one Scottish canteen.

Face recognition was long held back by the need for manual input of key points, such as the shape of the nose, mouth and chin, a process that proved prone to error. It only took off after 1988, when the Eigenface technique became available, using fewer than 100 points of identification to encode a standard facial image that could be compared against a database. Photographic recognition of faces

Head on
Automated facial recognition systems rely on unchanging aspects of the face, such as the distance between the eyes. A digital camera linked to a computer processes the image. The most reliable results are with 3-D images, but these are more expensive to produce.

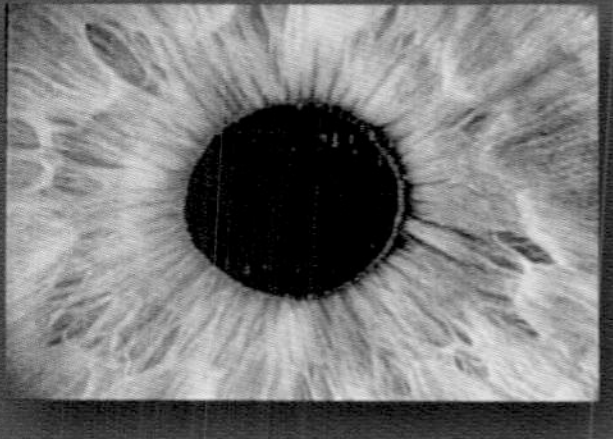

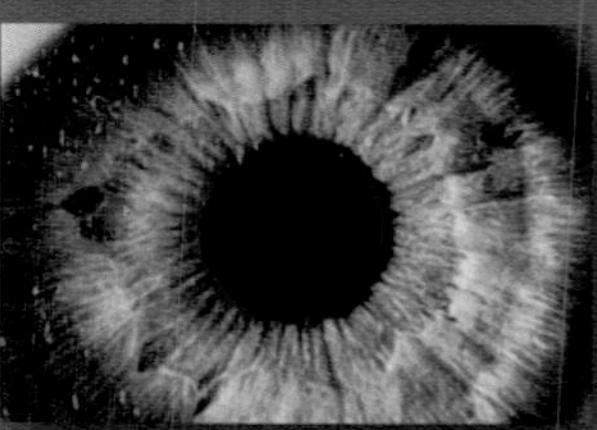

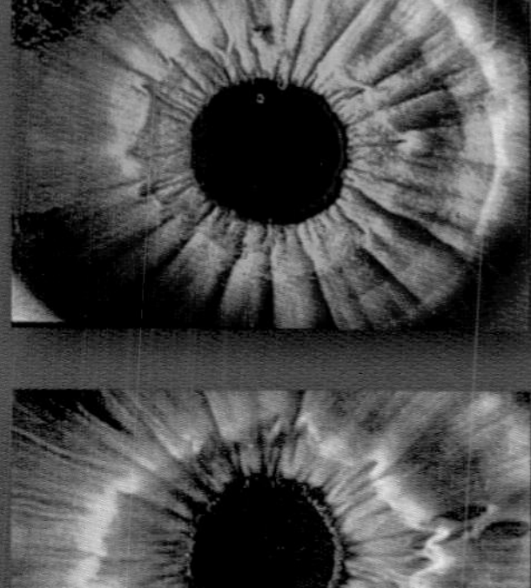

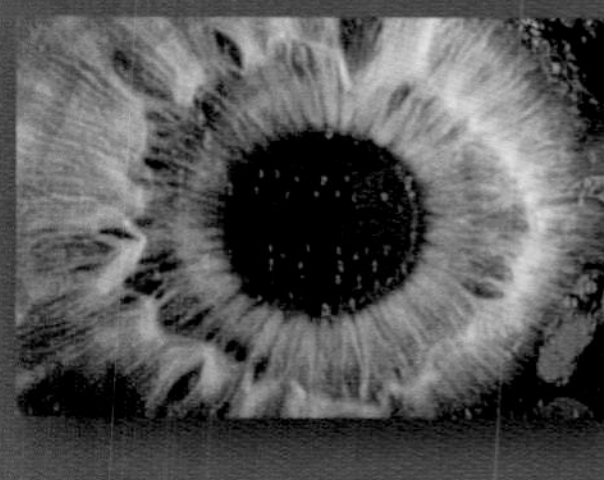

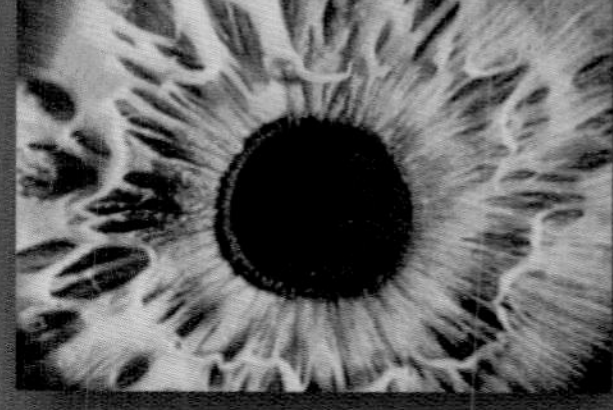

followed just three years later. Despite a relatively high rate of error (about 4 per cent), this technique has been put to use, enabling machines to replace people in casino security systems.

Procedures based on the morphology of the eye have proved more foolproof. Research undertaken from the 1930s on has shown that the pattern of the iris and of the blood vessels surrounding the retina are specific to each individual. The first commercial retinal scanner was developed in 1984 by a firm called EyeDentify. In 1987 the ophtalmologists Léonard Flom and Aran Safir took out a patent on an iris-recognition technique that was commercially deployed from 1995 on.

Although eye-recognition procedures have proved trustworthy, they also have disadvantages that have held back their use, notably high cost and the inconveniences of putting them to use. Retinal recognition, for example, involves holding the head still and looking into a camera at close range while an infrared beam sweeps across the eyeball. As a result, the techniques are reserved almost exclusively for high-security applications.

Exploring every avenue

To believe television crime dramas, DNA fingerprinting is the ultimate in modern-day identification technology. Almost infallible, it has been put to use since 1986, when the development of polymerase chain reaction (PCR) techniques made it possible to make identifications from tiny amounts of DNA. The only obvious drawback is the possibility of either accidental or deliberate contamination of the samples tested.

Behavioural analysis is also the subject of ongoing research. Voice recognition, drawing on speech rhythms, speed of utterance and other behavioural parameters, remains an inexact science, given that people's voices change with their emotional state as well as with sickness, fatigue and other factors. Even so, it has potential in the field of telephony. Signature recognition has evolved to take account of the dynamics of handwriting (the speed of the strokes, pressure on the pen and other factors), but it still remains at the lower end of the reliability spectrum. In short, no perfect system yet exists, and it is a reasonably sure bet that other avenues currently being explored, based on ears, body odour, gait and skin pores as well as thermal imaging, will also have downsides.

Even so, biometrics remains a growth area. The terrorist threat and the upsurge in global travel have made the question of controlling entry and exit into their territories crucially important for governments. And given the exponential growth of information systems, telephones and Internet commerce, use of biometric identifiers to supplement or replace passwords is another key issue. Any or all of the techniques described above could be put to use: it is simply a matter of finding the right combination of public acceptability, security, ease of use and cost.

RECOGNISING KEYSTROKES

One recently introduced computer security technique employs software to analyse the way in which different individuals' fingers strike the letters on their keyboard when accessing data. Designed to supplement passwords, the process causes minimum inconvenience and does not require expensive machinery. But users have to be careful not to get distracted while using the computer and must always use the same keyboard.

Eye to eye
Scanned images of irises are increasingly being put to use to provide secure access to telephones and computers.

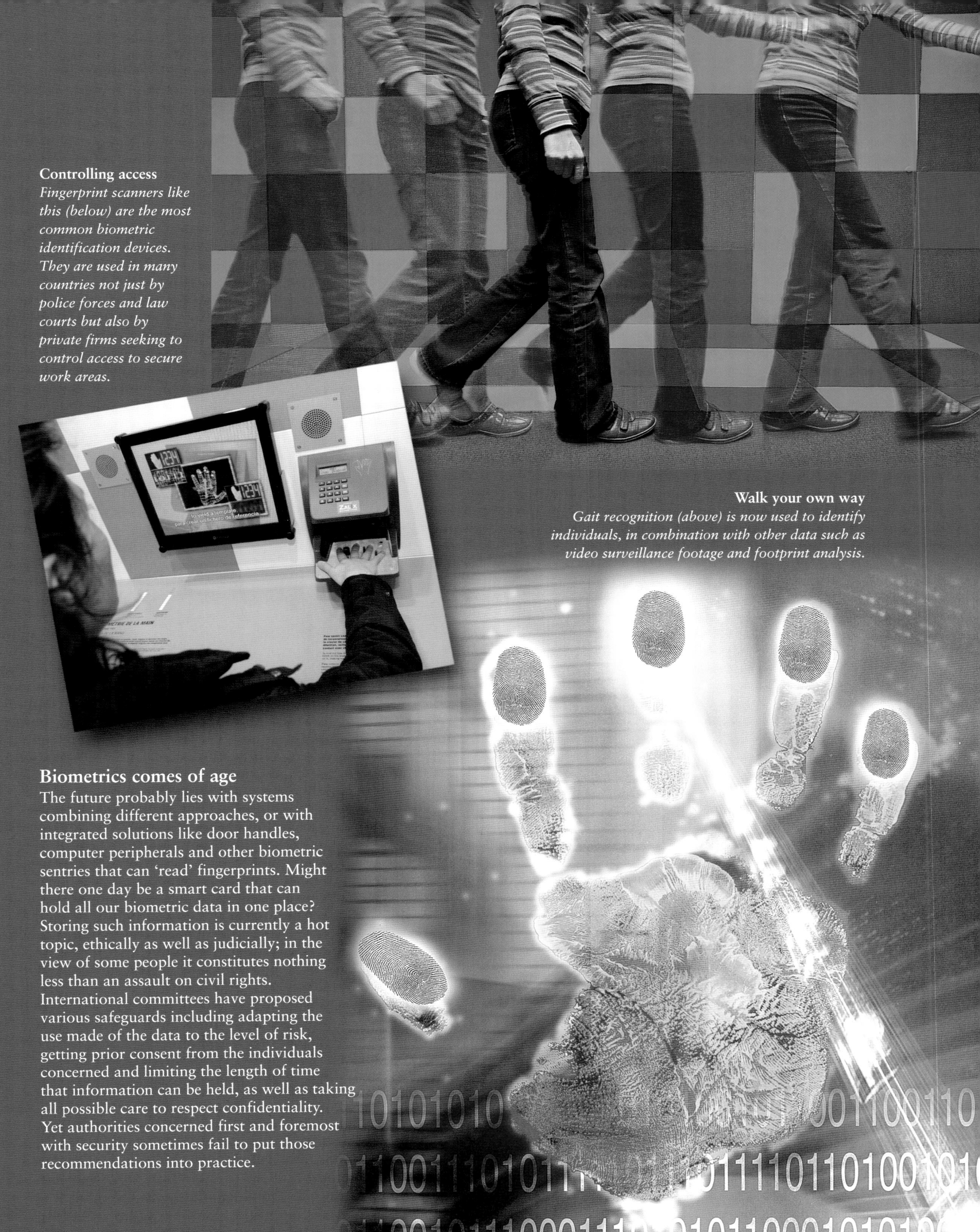

Controlling access
Fingerprint scanners like this (below) are the most common biometric identification devices. They are used in many countries not just by police forces and law courts but also by private firms seeking to control access to secure work areas.

Walk your own way
Gait recognition (above) is now used to identify individuals, in combination with other data such as video surveillance footage and footprint analysis.

Biometrics comes of age

The future probably lies with systems combining different approaches, or with integrated solutions like door handles, computer peripherals and other biometric sentries that can 'read' fingerprints. Might there one day be a smart card that can hold all our biometric data in one place? Storing such information is currently a hot topic, ethically as well as judicially; in the view of some people it constitutes nothing less than an assault on civil rights. International committees have proposed various safeguards including adapting the use made of the data to the level of risk, getting prior consent from the individuals concerned and limiting the length of time that information can be held, as well as taking all possible care to respect confidentiality. Yet authorities concerned first and foremost with security sometimes fail to put those recommendations into practice.

Setting speed records for passenger boats

Since the 1960s, constructors have sought ways of speeding up boats to produce vessels that could compete with aircraft. So-called 'wave-piercers' cut through the water with much of the hull remaining below the surface, reducing stress on the vessel and giving passengers a smoother ride at speed. In 1996 the French ferry company SNCM introduced two such vessels, the *Asco* and the *Aliso*, into service between Nice and Corsica. Averaging 36-37 knots (42mph), they cut the journey time almost in half.

Annual contest
The ferry race in Sydney Harbour (above) is a regular feature of Australia Day, celebrated on 26 January each year.

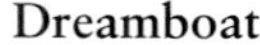

Dreamboat
The Techno SuperLiner, *shown here (above) in an artist's impression, was a Japanese project designed to carry 800 people at a speed of 55mph. The development was abandoned in 2005 and the vessel never became a reality.*

Today the term 'high-speed craft' is generally applied to vessels with average speeds above 30 knots (35mph), whether employing monohull, catamaran or trimaran designs. Most are thin-hulled catamarans with prows shaped to minimise the impact of swell.

Different designs

An alternative type of high-speed craft makes use of the phenomenon of lift, raising the hull partly or entirely out of the water. The best-known of these are the hovercraft, which are borne aloft on a cushion of air that removes virtually all water resistance. This category also includes boats with hulls designed to ride the waves, lifting the vessels out of the water so they can travel faster.

Then there are the hydrofoils, which employ wing-like structures mounted on struts attached to the hull. At low speed the hull rides in the water, but when the vessel accelerates it rises up on the foils, lifting much of the hull out of the water. Since the early 1970s Boeing has built some two dozen 929 Jetfoils – hydrofoils powered by water jets – which have seen service in the Royal Navy and other military operations, and also as ferries on regular routes, for instance in the Canary Islands and between Hong Kong and Macau.

There are also hybrid high-speed craft known as surface effect ships (SESs) or sidewall hovercraft. These are usually twin-hulled catamarans equipped with special motors to provide an air cushion. The air expelled between the twin hulls reduces drag and also the amount of water displaced.

High performance – at a cost

In the final decade of the 20th century as many as 400 high-speed craft were in use around the world, mostly as ferries, but since then their numbers have dwindled. One problem has been that the vessels have proved weather-dependent, providing uncomfortable rides in heavy swells. Another is their relatively small size, which means they have difficulty

Cross-Channel link
A poster for a cross-Channel hydrofoil service that for a time linked London with Ostend in Belgium.

meeting high-season demand for places. Yet the main constraint on their use has been fuel consumption, the more so as they need refined products that are more expensive than the crude fuels that power most ferries. At its top speed of 42 knots (48mph) the *Scorpio*, a high-speed ferry operated by Tirrenia from the Italian mainland to Sardinia, used 14 tonnes of fuel on each trip. It is no longer in service.

So have high-speed craft reached the end of the road? Many of those built for passenger services are now out of commission. Maritime companies prefer traditional ferries, which use less fuel while carrying more passengers and, crucially, cars. Future high-speed development now rests in the hands of the military, notably in the USA, where fast, large-scale troop carriers are being tested.

PUMP-JET POWER

As in most high-speed craft, the engines of the *Asco* (right) and its sister-boat the *Aliso* were each linked to a pump-jet. Also known as water jets, these pump water under the hull, passing it through a turbine before expelling it at high speed behind the vessel. The jets form an integral part of the hull, and compared with propulsion systems based on propellers and rudders they considerably reduce drag caused by water resistance. If the vessel needs to change direction or go backwards, the jet is simply turned or reversed. Pump-jets are also used on Jet Skis and other personal watercraft (PWCs). They are particularly effective at speeds above 25 knots (29mph).

Mechanically enhanced man

Technology evolves exponentially, as the 20th century has proved. A centenarian born at the end of the 19th century would have seen the advent of motorised transport, aviation, radio, television, the Space Age, information technology and genetics, among other life-changing innovations. By the end of the century, and with it the 2nd millennium AD, people were starting to ask if a new species of human being, *Homo technologicus,* was in its birth throes.

Citizens of industrialised lands today live in a world that is increasingly ruled by technology. In our homes, a whole array of white goods has reduced the amount of time needed for household tasks. Over the years, houses have filled up with electronic leisure equipment, ranging from DVD players and video game consoles to flat-screen television sets, plus other gadgets designed to increase our comfort and security. The 'smart home' is already on the horizon, with computer software programmed, among other functions, to use weather-forecasting data to adjust the central heating, turn lights off in empty rooms, or even warn parents if a child gets too close to a cooker.

Technology has dramatically changed the workplace and is changing working patterns. Psion put the first personal digital assistant (PDA) on the market in 1986, which from 1995 on was challenged by the Palm Pilot. Videoconferencing has reduced the need to travel to meetings, saving businesses substantial expense. For some employees, telecommuting has become a new way of working from home. In industry, after the initial heavy investment, robots are cheaper to employ and often more efficient than human workers, providing a possible solution for firms facing competition from countries with low labour costs.

A key sector for technology is the motor industry. From fuel injection to lighting by way of suspension control and tyre-pressure monitoring, not to mention airbags and central locking, electronic devices have made modern cars veritable computers on wheels. The Peugeot 607, launched in 1999, contained as many electronic components as the Airbus

Cyborg
A motorised exoskeleton (right) built by the Italian PERCRO (short for Perceptual Robotics) research laboratory. It allows the user to perform 28 separate energy-saving manoeuvres and is designed for use in difficult environments.

Control panel
A home automation control screen (below) monitors a house in a 6-acre suburb of ecological housing in the city of Lyon in France.

THE MILLENNIUM BUG THAT WASN'T

Computers going crazy, airports and hospitals paralysed, nuclear missiles out of control, stock exchanges in chaos ... In the late 1990s some IT experts predicted that all this and more would result as we entered the new millennium at midnight on 31 December, 1999. A programming error, they claimed, would cause clocks in computers to switch to 00 rather than 2000, causing the greatest catastrophe of modern times. In fact the Millennium Bug did not bite, yet the threat of computer breakdown remains a real one. In January 2010, a systems failure temporarily disabled almost half of all Germany's debit cards.

Superspecs
A composite picture (right) shows someone wearing computer-enhanced spectacles with a GPS mapping capability.

A310 had just 15 years earlier. And with the spread of global positioning system (GPS) devices, satellite navigation has taken over the task of route-planning and navigation by road atlas for many motorists.

A connected world

Personal computers have proved great time-savers for the technologically minded, with a wide range of uses from preparing accounts and editing texts to indexing record collections. When the first generation of PCs equipped with CD-ROM readers came on the market, it became possible to consult encyclopaedias from the kitchen table or armchair, to take virtual tours of museums and to lose oneself in video games whose graphics kept on getting more sophisticated.

The emergence of the World Wide Web made all this and more possible online as people learned to surf the Internet. But above all, it introduced a new era of 'all to all' communication, as opposed to the 'one to one' mode of telephones and the 'one to all' style of mass media like radio and television. Along with electronic mail, better known as email, this gigantic database crammed with words, sounds and images revolutionised person-to-person communication. With just a few clicks, anyone could address the world at large – and the world could respond. This quantum leap in communications did not come without some irritating inconveniences, such as junk e-mail and network breakdowns, and even personal risk from cybercrime, the release of confidential information and the spreading of malicious gossip. But it was a development that people embraced wholeheartedly.

Mobile phones have also profoundly changed behaviour patterns. As the devices got smaller, they were simultaneously enriched with applications, ranging from texting and multimedia messaging services to MP3 players, radios, cameras, games, television, Internet access, e-mails and GPS navigation. By scanning barcodes into a phone app it is even possible to shop online for ingredients delivered in a daily recipe application. Provided a signal is available, mobiles have made it simple to call anyone from almost anyhere, whether to change an appointment or call a taxi.

The digital age

It is becoming increasingly hard to escape from technology now that the entire planet has been transformed into a digitised global village. We still like to think that we can sometimes get away from it all to some unspoiled paradise, but we reach it by travelling on aeroplanes crammed with electronics. Once there, we record the sights on digital cameras, listen to our favourite music taken with us on MP3

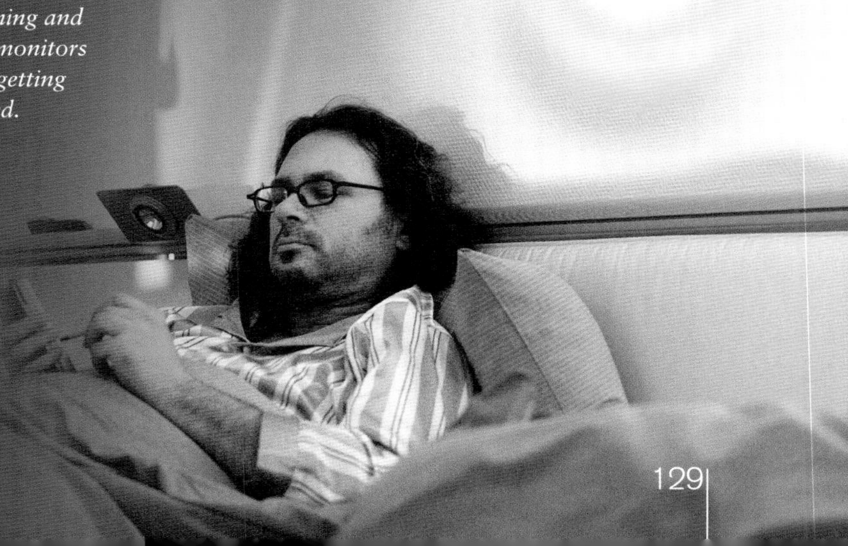

Smart house
Future homeowners will, if they wish, be able to access radio, television and the Internet from anywhere in the house. They will also be able to control heating, air conditioning and security monitors without getting out of bed.

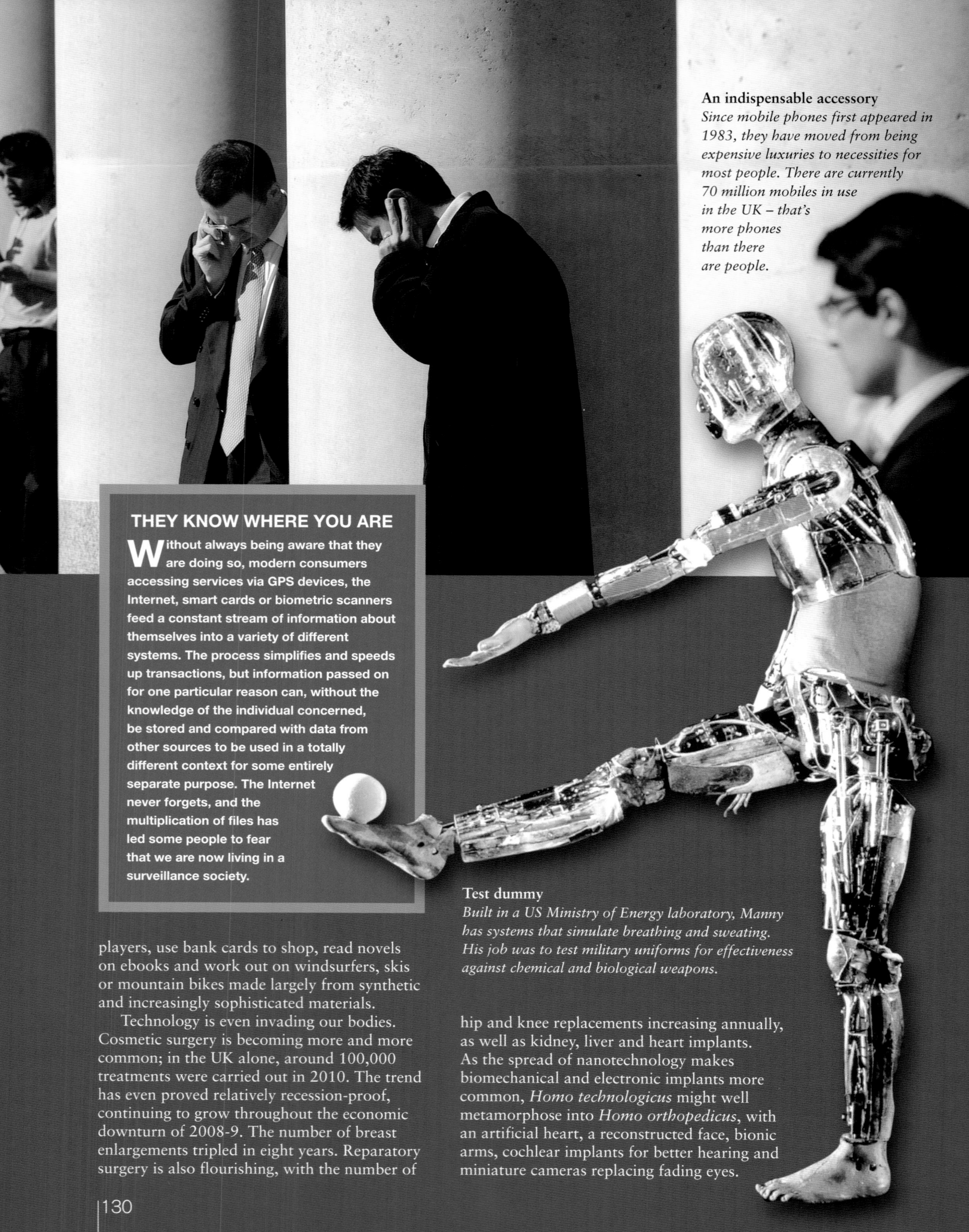

An indispensable accessory
Since mobile phones first appeared in 1983, they have moved from being expensive luxuries to necessities for most people. There are currently 70 million mobiles in use in the UK – that's more phones than there are people.

THEY KNOW WHERE YOU ARE

Without always being aware that they are doing so, modern consumers accessing services via GPS devices, the Internet, smart cards or biometric scanners feed a constant stream of information about themselves into a variety of different systems. The process simplifies and speeds up transactions, but information passed on for one particular reason can, without the knowledge of the individual concerned, be stored and compared with data from other sources to be used in a totally different context for some entirely separate purpose. The Internet never forgets, and the multiplication of files has led some people to fear that we are now living in a surveillance society.

Test dummy
Built in a US Ministry of Energy laboratory, Manny has systems that simulate breathing and sweating. His job was to test military uniforms for effectiveness against chemical and biological weapons.

players, use bank cards to shop, read novels on ebooks and work out on windsurfers, skis or mountain bikes made largely from synthetic and increasingly sophisticated materials.

Technology is even invading our bodies. Cosmetic surgery is becoming more and more common; in the UK alone, around 100,000 treatments were carried out in 2010. The trend has even proved relatively recession-proof, continuing to grow throughout the economic downturn of 2008-9. The number of breast enlargements tripled in eight years. Reparatory surgery is also flourishing, with the number of hip and knee replacements increasing annually, as well as kidney, liver and heart implants. As the spread of nanotechnology makes biomechanical and electronic implants more common, *Homo technologicus* might well metamorphose into *Homo orthopedicus*, with an artificial heart, a reconstructed face, bionic arms, cochlear implants for better hearing and miniature cameras replacing fading eyes.

Improving eyesight
A surgeon performing delicate eye surgery with the aid of a microscope (below). Devices are being developed to combat a range of eye problems, from long and shortsightedness to cataracts.

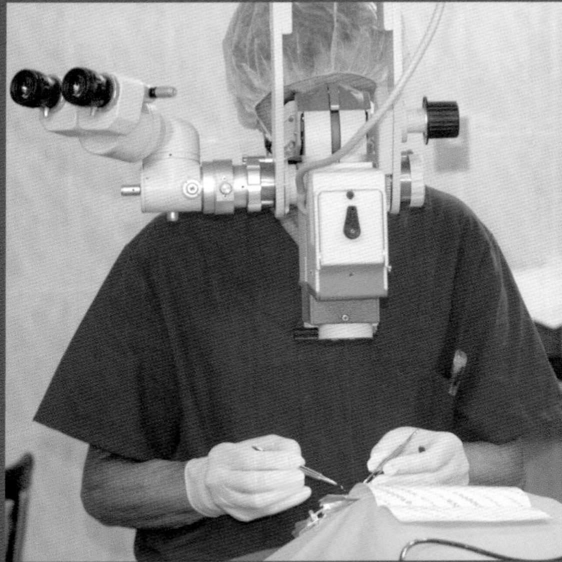

Terminator technology
In the second of James Cameron's Terminator trilogy, the 1991 film Terminator 2: Judgment Day, *Arnold Schwarzenegger (right) plays the eponymous cyborg who helps the humans resisting Skynet, an artificial intelligence system intent on destroying the human race. His opponent, the more advanced T-1000 Terminator model, is made of liquid metal and can change shape at will.*

It is hard to deny that we have benefited from the technological progress in our daily environment, but there has been a cost in terms of dependence on ever-more-complex systems that are sometimes hard to understand. When these systems break down, individuals can find themselves isolated, with no-one to turn to for advice or to take responsibility for a malfunction. The proliferation of new information technologies has done much to minimise the significance of physical distance. Yet there is no clear evidence that the increased flow of information from ever-more-efficient media has led to greater understanding or improved our ability to talk to, share with and live comfortably alongside our fellow human beings.

VIRTUAL MONEY

Money becomes invisible when it is lodged in a computer's memory or in a smart card chip. Yet it is still very much there, even if it cannot be seen or touched like cash. All the signs suggest that *Homo technologicus* of the future is destined to live in a cash-free society, in which mobile phones may become the principal means of making payments. Yet even if money turns completely virtual, it will still retain its functions as a standard of value and a means of exchange.

Counterfeit note detectors 1995

Fraud hunters
Experts scan a magnified $100 bill for signs of counterfeiting. Inset: Dufils's detector at work on a 100 euro note.

In 1995 a Frenchman named Stéphane Dufils developed a digital counterfeit note detector that he marketed as *Incontournable* ('Indispensable'). The device analysed the material of which the currency was made and the quality of the watermarks, using two light sources simultaneously to reveal defects.

The very first counterfeit detector was invented by an American, Robert Williams Wood, back in 1903. Most detectors today work on the same principles as the black light of Wood's lamps. The devices filter out all but the violet and ultraviolet rays nearest the visible part of the spectrum, showing up synthetic fibres as fluorescent. Genuine paper money, made up of 100 per cent cellulose, remains unaffected when exposed to black light, but the lower-grade paper typically used by counterfeiters triggers the fluorescence. Some notes – pounds and euros among them – incorporate features in an ink that is invisible in natural light but that shows up when exposed to ultraviolet.

Extra precautions

There are other ways of highlighting fakes, ranging from the use of infrared light to the incorporation of security threads in genuine banknotes. Since the year 2000, higher-denomination sterling notes have included such features as areas of micro lettering that can only be read under a magnifying glass. Infrared detectors are used to verify the presence and accuracy of infrared markings on the notes. The metallic thread running through the note may include magnetic elements that can be checked to ensure that the currency is authentic. Holograms have also become more widely used as the threat of counterfeiting has grown. In 2009 the Bank of England revealed that more than half a million forged notes were in circulation in the UK, 95 per cent of them £20 denominations. With a total of 2.6 billion notes in use, that figure represents roughly one fake note for every 5,000 good ones.

DETECTION PENS

Counterfeit banknote detection pens have been available since 1991. They contain an iodine-based ink that reacts with the starch contained in the wood-based paper employed for poor-quality counterfeit notes to produce a black mark. Used on the fibre-based paper in genuine banknotes, they leave no stain. But the pens cannot detect fakes printed on fibre-based paper.

Electronic money 1995

In the late 1980s various financial institutions developed ways in which money could be stored digitally, allowing accounts to be settled and bills paid via purpose-built payment terminals. In contrast to standard debit cards, the stored-value cards that came into use actually 'contained' the money in digitised form, rather than simply serving as intermediaries between the tradesman and the user's bank account.

In September 1992 the system was first tested on a large scale in Denmark in the form of prepaid cards that were not rechargeable. Then, in 1995, Belgium integrated the Proton smart-card system with existing debit cards, intending it to cover day-to-day living expenses. The cards could be topped up from a current account at bank terminals.

Dematerialising money

In 1999, inspired by the Proton system, France introduced the Monéo electronic purse. This system ensured that users who kept the cards topped up always had enough money on them to cover small transactions, doing away with the need to carry a number of different smart cards to pay for specific services such as parking or telephone calls. The Monéo cards were simple to use – there was no requirement for a code or pin number when paying for something. Businesses liked the arrangement: the cards were convenient, they reduced the need for small change and also cut down on the quantity of notes accumulating in their tills, reducing the risk of theft or attacks on staff, as well as of customers being short-changed. Yet high running costs and public concerns about the system's security meant that Monéo enjoyed only limited success, failing to take the place of credit cards. The future of prepaid and stored-value cards lies in linking them to online accounts or to supports like USB flash drives or mobile phones.

TELEPHONE CARDS

Before the days of the mobile phone, when telephone boxes were the only way to make calls while out and about, prepaid telephone cards were invented, doing away with the need to carry change. The first were introduced in Italy in 1976 to combat vandalism of public telephones. Prepaid cards bearing magnetic authorisation strips were introduced into Britain, Austria, Sweden and France the following year and quickly became popular, but similar cards did not launch in the USA until 1987.

Coffee card
(Below) The Belgian Proton card was one of the first prepaid cash cards to go into service. Since that time the use of electronic money has spread widely. In 2005 a Japanese company introduced a system of payment by mobile phone.

CARL SAGAN – 1934 TO 1996

Ambassador for the stars

Some scientists shine as media personalities without compromising their professional integrity. One such was Carl Sagan. Through interviews, lectures, books and TV, he conveyed to the public his own fascination with the strangeness and beauty of the universe. He was an exceptional ambassador for astronomy.

Carl Sagan was born in Brooklyn, New York, the son of Ukrainian immigrants. He was just seven years old when he fell under the spell of science while thumbing through a book about astronomy in a public library. He would later describe the experience as like feeling a sort of vertigo. How could those gigantic bodies remain suspended in that immense black void?

In 1961 he published an article in the journal *Science*, outlining a proposal of how to terraform Venus to make it suitable for habitation. The idea involved injecting algae into the atmosphere of this seeringly hot planet to change carbon dioxide into oxygen; solar shades would reduce the amount of solar radiation reaching the planet and block the heating effects of solar wind. In 1971, as a professor of astronomy and space science at Cornell University in New York State, he took charge of the university's laboratory for planetary studies.

Message to the stars
The Voyager *Golden Records – videodiscs placed on board the twin* Voyager *probes that have now travelled beyond our Solar System – include pictograms designed to show any extraterrestrials that might encounter them how to play the discs and where they came from.*

Lunar landscape
Carl Sagan in Death Valley, California, with a model of the Viking *Mars lander.*

SCI-FI BEST-SELLER

Sagan based his best-selling science- fiction novel *Contact*, published in 1985, on the work of Jill Tarter, director of SETI's Project Phoenix. In 1997 Robert Zemeckis based a film starring Jodie Foster on the book.

LISTENING TO THE COSMOS

To capture radio signals that might be dispatched by some hypothetical extraterrestrial civilisation, in 1984 Carl Sagan founded the SETI Institute (the acronym stands for Search for Extraterrestrial Intelligence) as a private non-profit-making organisation. Its goal was to 'lend an ear' to the thousand stars closest to Earth bearing some resemblance to our Sun, using the giant radio telescope near Arecibo in Puerto Rico (above) as a listening device. So far, no signals of any kind have been received from our postulated far-flung neighbours.

Messages for extraterrestrials

At the time the US–Soviet space race was in full swing. As an adviser to NASA, Sagan was involved in the preparation of the Mariner, Viking, Voyager and Galileo missions. On 2 March, 1972, the *Pioneer 10* space probe set off for Jupiter, soon to be followed by *Pioneer 11*. The *Pioneer* crafts were the first man-made objects designed to eventually leave the Solar System. On board each was a gold-plated aluminium plaque bearing the image of a naked man and woman, alongside diagrammatic representations of the Solar System and a hydrogen atom. Sagan had designed the panels to serve as messages to any intelligent extraterrestrials who might one day encounter the vessels.

In 1977 Sagan went further. He equipped the two *Voyager* probes launched in August and September that year with videodiscs containing, among other items, a collection of 116 images portraying the diversity of life on Earth, an eclectic collection of music, the word 'Hello' spoken in 55 different languages, and a message from then US President Jimmy Carter.

Multimedia man

Marrying together the physical and life sciences, Sagan was to become one of the foremost proponents of the science of exobiology – the study of the origin, evolution and distribution of life in the universe. In his writings he was equally scathing about science-fiction writers who chose to see 'little green men' everywhere and sceptics who denied the very possibility of any form of extraterrestrial life. Sagan's skills as a populariser made him a best-selling author, notably with *Cosmic Connection: An Extraterrestrial Perspective*, published in 1973, and *The Dragons of Eden*, a brilliant study of the evolution of human intelligence that won him the Pulitzer Prize five years later. Not content to rest on his laurels, he turned his acute business sense and talents as a storyteller to similarly good effect on television. More than 500 million viewers in 60 countries watched *Cosmos*, a 13-part series with a $9 million budget, conceived and presented by Sagan himself. A book of the same name that accompanied the series was on the *New York Times* bestseller list for 70 weeks.

Sagan may have dreamed of seeing human beings set foot on Mars, but he did not forget the importance of Earth. In his later works he became a passionate spokesman for the planet and the need to protect our environment. Over the years he was laden with honours, but his health was fatally undermined by myelodysplasia, a form of bone marrow cancer. He passed away on 20 December, 1996, at the age of 62. Four years later, the International Astronomical Union paid him homage by naming a crater near the equator of Mars, the landing site of the 1997 Mars Pathfinder spacecraft, in his honour.

Earth calling
In 1974 Sagan and his fellow American astronomer Frank Drake used the Arecibo radio telescope (above) to direct a message at Messier 13, a 300,000-strong star cluster some 25,000 light-years from Earth.

In search of other Earths

Satellites revolving around stars other than the Sun are known as exoplanets. Combining patience and scientific astuteness, astronomers are seeking to find ones resembling Earth that might conceivably harbour life.

51 Pegasi b
Shown here in an artist's impression, this exoplanet is extraordinarily close to its star, lying 20 times closer to 51 Pegasi than our Earth does to the Sun.

Claims of exoplanet findings had been made since the 19th century, but it was not until 1988 that the first feasible discovery – of a planet orbiting the binary star Gamma Cephei – was published by a group of Canadian astronomers. It took until 2002, and the introduction of new techniques, for their findings to be confirmed. In 1992 Polish radio astronomer Aleksander Wolszczan and Canadian Dale Frail discovered an exoplanet orbiting a pulsar, but the first detection of an exoplanet orbiting a main sequence star was announced on 6 October, 1995, by Swiss astronomers Michel Mayr and Didier Queloz. The body they had identified was circling the star 51 Pegasi, in the Pegasus constellation 50.9 light-years from Earth. It circled the star every four days and had a mass approximately half that of Jupiter's, indicating that it was probably a gas giant. At the time, the only known planets were the eight orbiting our own Sun. The discovery rekindled hope that life might someday be found beyond Earth.

Means of detection

Finding an exoplanet is difficult, because any brightness it gives off is drowned out by that of the star it orbits. The two Swiss researchers employed what is known as the radial velocity method. To get some idea of this, picture two people joining hands to spin round in a circle: they spin round a central point located somewhere between them. Watching from a fixed point, an observer sees first one, then the other, as they move closer and further away, swinging around the central hub. The same phenomenon occurs when an exoplanet revolves around a star: both move around a common centre of mass. The radial velocity method involves measuring the changes in the star's movements brought about by the gravitational pull of the exoplanet or planets.

The to-and-fro movement of the star is usually minuscule, so the measurement is difficult to make. In 1995 techniques became sufficiently sophisticated to make the process feasible and today it is the most commonly used approach, responsible for the discovery of 90 per cent of exoplanets known so far. The main alternative technique concentrates on the phenomenon of transit, observing the dip in a star's brightness when a planet passes between it and the Earth, hiding part of its light.

Classifying the discoveries

By early 2010 more than 420 exoplanets had been detected, the closest little more than 10 light-years from Earth, the furthest more than 20,000 light-years distant. Some stars

have several orbiting planets. Some planets revolve around more than one star, in effect having two or three different suns. The biggest planets and those closest to their stars are the easiest to detect, for these have the biggest effects on the star's trajectory or luminosity. Scientists estimate that up to 20 per cent of stars resembling our Sun have one or more gas giants circling around them, while at least 40 per cent have smaller bodies like the Earth.

A classification system has begun to emerge for this multiplication of heavenly bodies. Exoplanets with a mass between one and ten

Gauging luminosity
The transit method of hunting exoplanets analyses the decline in a star's brightness – illustrated above by the yellow line – noted when a planet passes between its star and the observing telescope.

OCEAN PLANETS

Entirely covered by water, ocean planets could feasibly harbour life. Marc Kuchner of NASA's Exoplanets and Stellar Astrophysics Laboratory envisaged their existence in 2003, as did Alain Léger of Paris Sud-11 University. Where might the water have come from? A planet that formed far from its star might be composed half of rock and half of ice, like comets or the dwarf planet of our own Solar System, Pluto. In the course of its formation, the planet could move nearer to or further away from its star. When nearer to the star, the ice might begin to melt, allowing a layer of water to cover the planet's surface, potentially to a depth of hundreds of miles. The mass of such a planet could not be more than ten times that of the Earth, as the force of gravity would transform the water into gas. One exoplanet that seems to meet all the necessary criteria to be an ocean planet is GJ 1214 b, some 40 light-years away in the Ophiuchus constellation, which has a mass 6.6 times that of Earth.

Detecting water
Variations in the absorption of light, as shown in the diagram below, indicate the presence of water vapour in the atmosphere of an exoplanet; this particular example is from planet HD 189733 b. The same planet and its star are seen here (right) as recorded by the Spitzer space telescope.

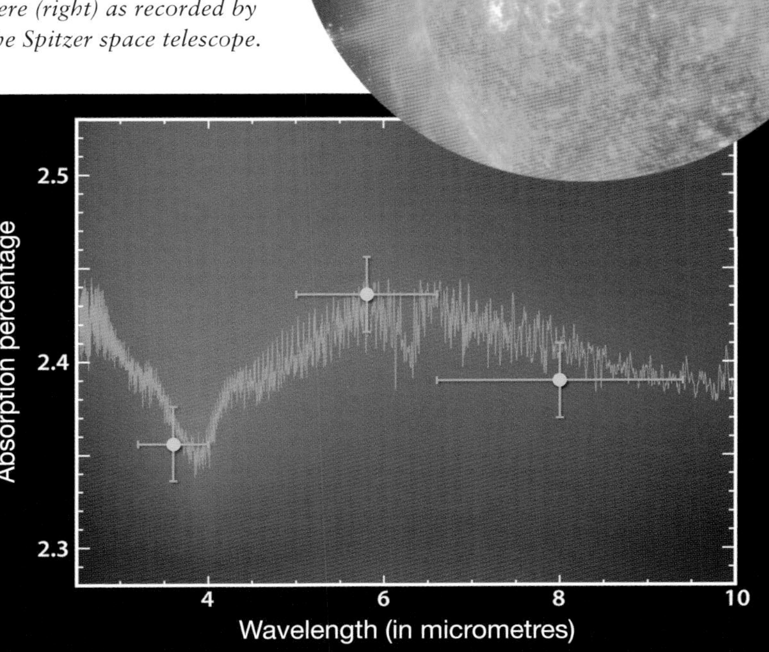

times that of Earth are called super-Earths. Those in close proximity to their star – defined as less than a tenth of the Earth's distance from the Sun – and with a mass equal to or exceeding Jupiter's are classed as hot Jupiters. Some are thought to be ocean planets (see box, page 137). Others, the chthonian planets, are the rocky cores of ancient gas giants whose atmospheres have been stripped away as a result of the close presence of a star.

Planet hunter
The COROT space telescope sends images back to Earth that are analysed by scientists in a network of stations at Kiruna (Sweden), Aussaguel (France), Hartebeesthoek (South Africa), Kourou (French Guiana), Alcantara (Brasil) and Vienna (Austria).

VERY SPECIAL MISSIONS

A number of missions designed to track down exoplanets have recently been launched using unmanned craft and space telescopes. The priority now is to locate small, Earth-like planets in the hope of finding signs of life. This can only be done from outside our planet's atmosphere, which interferes with observations made from Earth. The European Space Agency, in collaboration with its French equivalent CNES, dispatched the COROT space telescope in December 2006. Using the transit method (see main text), the craft has proved sufficiently sensitive to detect rocky planets of Earth-like dimensions, as shown by the discovery of the exoplanet COROT-7 b in 2009. NASA's Kepler mission, launched in March 2009, is taking a similar approach and by 2011 had discovered five exoplanets, the smallest of them 20 times larger than Earth.

Very hot spot
COROT-7 b lies closer to its star than any other known exoplanet. Astronomers reckon that the daytime temperature must reach 2,000° C.

EXOBIOLOGY

Exobiology is the study of the processes that lead to the appearance and evolution of life, whether on Earth at the time of our planet's formation or elsewhere in the universe. Could exoplanets harbour life? There is obviously a chance that they can, otherwise life, including human beings, would not be here on Earth. One of the preconditions for life is that the planet must be in a habitable zone – in other words, a region around a star where water could remain in a liquid state, for that element seems to be crucial to any form of life as we know it.

For that to be the case, the planet must be at the right distance from its star, neither too close, in which case the water would evaporate, nor too far away, causing the water to freeze into ice. The Earth is well placed in relation to the Sun in comparison with, say, Venus, which is too near, or Jupiter, which is too distant.

Among the exoplanets discovered to date, Gliese 581 c and Gliese 581 d, 20 light-years away in the constellation of Libra, are the two currently considered most promising in this respect. To detect any possibility of life, astronomers analyse the light that the planets emit in an attempt to discover tell-tale biological signatures such as the presence of methane, oxygen or chlorophyll. So far no evidence of a likely candidate has been found, but there is good reason to hope that one might figure among the great discoveries of the 21st century.

Distant sunrise
An artist's impression of dawn on Gliese 581 c (top), the exoplanet currently thought most closely to resemble the Earth.

Record breakers

Some exoplanets have attracted particular attention. PSR B1620-26 b, located 5,600 light-years from Earth in the Scorpio constellation, is reckoned to be the oldest detected, dating back 12.7 billion years almost to the birth of the universe. It is also one of only three exoplanets known to orbit a binary star system. At 1,400 light-years away, in the Hercules constellation, is TrES-4, the biggest so far discovered with a diameter 1.7 times that of Jupiter, the largest planet in our Solar System; yet its density, at 0.2g/cm^3, is similar to that of balsa wood. In contrast, in the Monoceros constellation is COROT-7 b, 490 light-years away and the smallest found to date, with a diameter just 1.7 times that of Earth. Yet for all that has been learned, no-one has so far been able to view an exoplanet in anything approaching the detail of the planets in our own Solar System. The first photographs show little more than coloured dots. Visiting the exoplanets remains unimaginable: to reach the nearest one would take our current space probes tens of thousands of years.

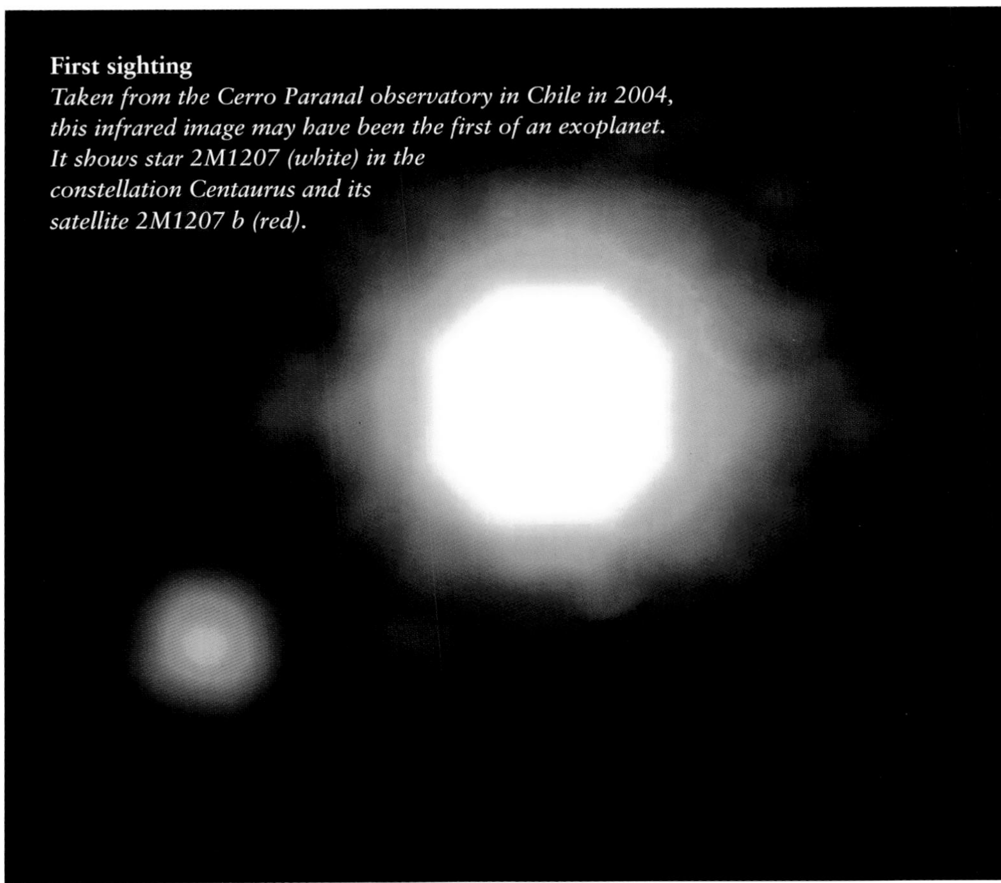

First sighting
Taken from the Cerro Paranal observatory in Chile in 2004, this infrared image may have been the first of an exoplanet. It shows star 2M1207 (white) in the constellation Centaurus and its satellite 2M1207 b (red).

SNAPSHOT OF NEW DELHI

Between tradition and high technology

India's capital, New Delhi, mounted the new technology bandwagon as the 21st century dawned. Today it is a sprawling, bustling metropolis of almost 15 million inhabitants and extreme contrasts, where mobile phones and Tata Nano cars exist side by side with elephants and wandering cows, bicycle rickshaws and pedal-powered milk deliverers.

Delhi has never cut its links with its past. The old town is still there, haunted by the echoes of ancient voices resounding from the walls of the historic Red Fort – the voices of Turkish sultans, Mughal emperors and Afghan potentates among them. This is a city of narrow alleyways and tiny shops, bazaars and beggars, ornate wooden balconies and smelly open sewers. To the south, the new town built during the British Raj speaks mostly English. With its wide avenues and formal gardens, its banks and administrative buildings, it almost feels like an architect's model of a 20th-century ideal city.

As recently as the 1980s, only a clear-eyed observer would have picked up any signs of the city's more intimate transformations. By the 1990s those signs were visible everywhere. Restaurants serving meat were becoming common in a vegetarian nation that had developed a taste for pork, chicken and, most surprisingly of all in the land of sacred cows, for beef. These new restaurants attracted a young clientele of businessmen, wearing ties in the Western manner, whose presence

New and old
Against the backdrop of a gleaming glass office building, workers in New Delhi mount scaffolding used in the construction of the Golden Quadrilateral Highway (left). The road links the city with Mumbai (aka Bombay), Kolkata (Calcutta) and Chennai (Madras). New Delhi's Jantar Mantar Observatory (below) was built in 1724 for the Maharaja of Jaipur.

proclaimed another, more profound revolution: that of an economic boom primed and fuelled by biotechnology, robotics and a burgeoning telecommunications industry.

High-tech boomtown

One man whose career has linked the two Delhis, old and new, is Kushal Pal Singh, the city's unchallenged property king. His curriculum vitae started typically enough for a child of the local elite. He studied in the UK and saw service in the Indian Army's prestigious Deccan Horse regiment before marrying into the founding family of a real estate concern, the DLF (Delhi Land and Finance). Eventually Kushal Pal Singh took the helm at DLF and set about buying up dry and dusty farmland in an area called Gurgaon on the fringe of the capital.

By the mid-1980s, high-tech enterprises were starting to transform the face of India and over the next decade they set down roots and grew rapidly. One city where these companies chose to set up shop was Bangalore; another was Delhi. Kushal Pal Singh sold them his wastelands in Gurgaon and they turned them into oases of lawns and fountains fit for IT specialists. Gurgaon became part of the Indian economic miracle – and made Kushal and the DLF a fortune. His personal wealth today is estimated at nearly $30 billion.

High-tech health

Naresh Trehan takes a place alongside Kushal Pal Singh among the harbingers of the new India. Trehan studied medicine in the USA, specialising in heart surgery. As well as developing his own physical dexterity as a surgeon, he gained a thorough knowledge of new technology and robotic surgical techniques, then returned to Delhi where he founded the Escorts Heart Institute and

CAR WASH

As India's car industry booms, the contrast of old and new can be seen in the cars on Delhi's streets. The old is represented by the Hindustan Ambassador, a sedan originally produced in the 1950s. Typical of the new is the compact and responsive Maruti, built by India's first mass-market car manufacturer with the budding middle class in mind. Since 2009 these models have been joined by the Tata Nano, a car that sells for less than £1,500. Whatever the car, it adds to Delhi's congestion and pollution, and is likely to spend long hours in traffic jams alongside animal-powered, pedal-powered and hand-hauled vehicles.

Street life
Bicycle rickshaws compete for business outside the Red Fort, built between 1636 and 1646 (above). This vast edifice, incorporating palaces, mosques and pavilions, was named a UNESCO World Heritage Site in 2007. Left: A typical Delhi street scene. According to the World Health Organisation, the Indian capital is the world's fourth most polluted city.

Solar pioneer
Kamla, seen above in 2007 shortly after gaining her diploma, is the Rajasthan region's first woman solar engineer. She started studying in night classes at the age of 11, while working by day as a field labourer and domestic help. Now she travels round rural areas installing solar panels.

Research Centre. The institute today enjoys international renown as one of the best cardiology centres in the world, with almost 50,000 successful open-heart surgery operations to its credit.

In the race for economic success, the health and drug sector has followed much the same pattern as computers and cars: individuals have recognised opportunities and turned them into extraordinary success. One such story is that of Sikh Malvinder Mohan Singh, whose grandfather was a Pakistani refugee who had a money-lending business in old Delhi. In 1972, in defiance of international agreements on intellectual property rights, the Indian government gave a green light to the nation's pharmaceutical laboratories to copy any new drug launched on the world market. Malvinder's family took full advantage of the state's new position. Over the ensuing decades they built up their Ranbaxy pharmaceutical laboratory into one of the most important on the planet. Malvinder ended up heading an enterprise employing some 9,000 people in 24 countries. In 2008 he and his brother Shivinder sold a majority stake in the company to Daiichi Sanyo of Japan for an estimated $4.6 billion.

Knowledge and fortune

Two goddesses are particularly venerated in Delhi: Saraswati, the goddess of knowledge, and Lakshmi, goddess of fortune. Sunil Bharti Mittal looked to both in building up what would become the world's fifth largest wireless company. After graduating from Punjab University, he first set up a bicycle parts business. But his intimate knowledge of old Delhi, at a time when finding a public telephone in working order was a challenge, convinced him that telecommunications was the future. In 1983 he marketed India's first push-button phones; ten years later he was selling the first mobiles. Today, his firm Bharti Airtel is the country's leading private operator.

Telephone wires carry more than just speech these days. E-mails soon followed, and Sabeer Bhatia provided the means to deliver them. His father was an officer in the Indian Army, his mother a senior bank official. Bhatia completed his studies in the USA, first at Caltech and then at Stanford University. A gifted student, he graduated with a Master's degree in electrical engineering. In 1992 he went to work for Apple, where he crossed paths with Jack Smith, a work colleague who soon became his business partner. The pair created Hotmail, which rapidly made itself the world's leading e-mail service. In 1997 Microsoft bought the site for $400 million.

A PASSION FOR CRICKET

Cinema may be Delhi's favourite amusement, but it is cricket that claims the city's hearts and minds. On important match days, the Jawaharlal Nehru Stadium fills up with 100,000 spectators who come to cheer on the national Test side. Posters of past masters like Australia's Donald Bradman can be seen alongside images of more recent home-grown greats, such as Sunil Gavaskar, competing for space on the walls of apartments with pictures of Aishwarya Rai, the 1994 Miss World, now a celebrated film actress. Leading cricketers such as Sachin Tendulkar rival top Bollywood stars in popularity.

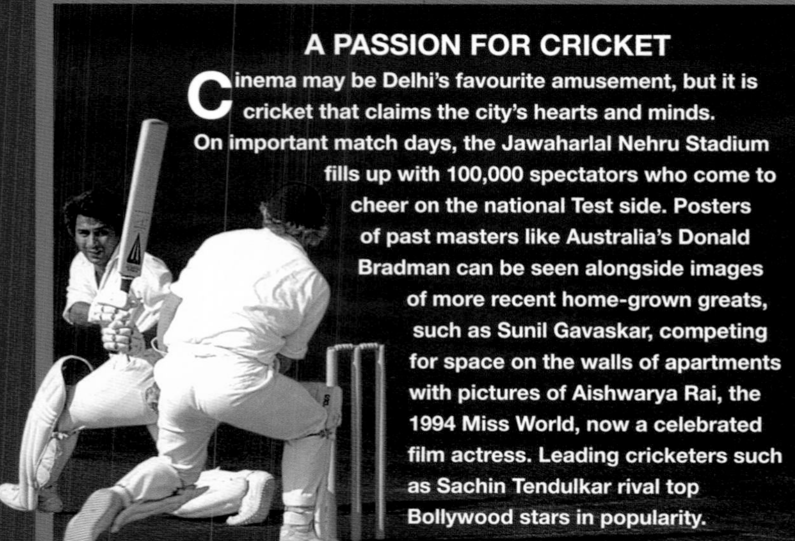

Technology and cinema

Video games, computer software, solar panels: India is seizing every opportunity the modern world has to offer. Delhi's young people study English and computing in the institutes that have sprung up across the city almost as fast as new restaurants. Their aim is to board the IT and technology bandwagon and make themselves a fortune. Many British businesses have taken advantage of these developments by moving their call centres to Delhi or other Indian cities, although by 2011 such moves were becoming less common.

For the young there is one over-riding diversion, the cinema, although films serve as life enhancers for Indians of all ages and classes. Bombay's Bollywood studios are among the world's principal centres of film production. In the Golcha, Shiela, Regal or any other of Delhi's 200 picture palaces, spectators stand for the national anthem before immersing themselves heart and soul in the drama played out on screen. Tickets cost anything from 30 to 200 rupees (40p to £2.50) – the price of seeing their god-like stars and hearing them speak and sing in any of the 26 languages used in the capital.

Faces of India
Located 20 miles south of Delhi, Gurgaon (left) is home to the largest concentration of commercial enterprises in India. The new town is linked to Delhi by an expressway and a metro. Below: Romance and violence, songs and dances, are the staples of the Indian cinema industry. Ninety per cent of the films shown in the capital are home produced.

A SEPARATE STATUS

Delhi's metropolitan area is a Union territory of the Republic of India, officially known as the National Capital Territory of Delhi. Its boundaries include a number of conjoined cities and villages divided for administrative purposes into nine separate districts. New Delhi, India's capital, is one of these districts, taking up 3 per cent of the territory's total land area.

THE WORLD'S BIGGEST FILM STAR

In 1999 BBC News Online held a millennium poll to find the greatest star of stage or screen. To the surprise of many, the runaway winner was Amitabh Bachchan, little known in the West but adored in his native India as the star of more than 140 films. Born in 1942, Bachchan rose to fame as the angry young man of Indian cinema, best known for playing troubled youths. Since then he has become an institution within the nation's movie industry, now sometimes starring alongside his son Abhishek.

COMIC CON

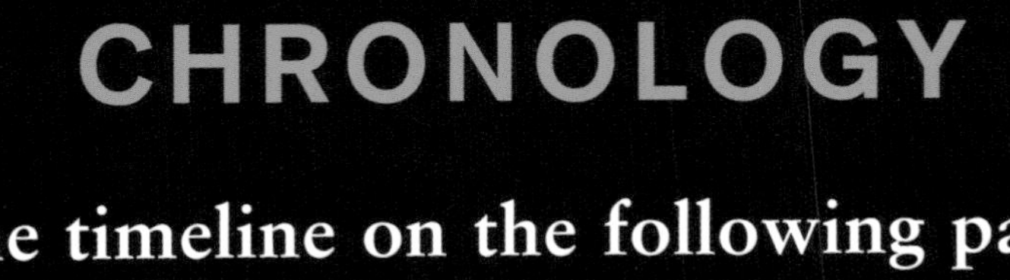

CHRONOLOGY

The timeline on the following pages records major discoveries, inventions and developments of the last two decades of the 20th century. Selected historical landmarks are included to provide chronological context for the scientific, technological and other innovations listed below them.

1982

EVENTS

- Britain defeats Argentina in the Falklands War
- Death of Soviet leader Leonid Brezhnev
- Helmut Kohl becomes chancellor of West Germany
- Israel occupies southern Lebanon; Hezbollah and Islamic Jihad emerge in response to the invasion

INVENTIONS

- American researchers isolate oncogenes (genes that can cause cancer)
- Sony and JVC develop the camcorder
- The mathematician Benoît Mandelbrot expounds the concept of fractals
- The US Air Force brings into service the Lockheed-Martin F-117A Nighthawk – the first aircraft to employ stealth technology
- Disney releases *Tron*, the first feature film to employ computer-generated imagery, to limited public acclaim
- 3-D television is tested in the USA and Europe
- A prototype chimney solar power station is built in Stuttgart, Germany, but solar energy will for the time being remain marginal as a power source

1983

EVENTS

- NATO deploys Pershing II missiles in Germany, triggering a nuclear alert in the Soviet Union
- Germany's Green Party wins its first seats in the federal parliament
- Israel and Lebanon sign the May 17 Agreement, a peace accord
- The USA invades Grenada, a British territory in the Caribbean

INVENTIONS

- A consortium of Swiss firms put the first Swatch wrist watches on the market
- Jacques Cousteau revives the turbosail, a wind-assisted propulsion system for ships, invented in 1924
- The AIDS virus is discovered
- The Motorola DynaTAC 8000X becomes the first cell phone to win Federal Communications Commission approval
- The McDonnell Douglas F/A-18 enters service as a multi-role jet fighter

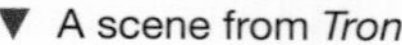

▼ A scene from *Tron*

▼ Comparing genetic fingerprints

1984

- India's prime minister, Indira Gandhi, is assassinated by Sikh extremists; the Army occupies the Golden Temple at Amritsar
- The miners' strike begins in Britain
- Toxic gas leak from the Union Carbide plant in Bhopal, India, kills over 2,000 and maims thousands more

- US surgeons working with biologists use skin grafts to save the lives of two badly burned children
- The development of tobacco plants genetically altered to incorporate a toxin poisonous to insects launches a debate about the merits and risks of genetic modification
- Measurements taken in Antarctica by Shigeru Chubachi of Japan alert the international community to the hole in the ozone layer
- Carl Sagan, professor of astronomy and space science at Cornell University and a leading proponent of the science of exobiology, founds the SETI (Search for Extraterrestrial Intelligence) Institute

1985

- The first Schengen accords are signed, opening up Europe's borders
- Mikhail Gorbachev becomes First Secretary of the Communist Party of the Soviet Union
- A state of emergency is declared in South Africa in response to anti-apartheid demonstrations

- Positron emission tomography (PET), a medical nuclear imaging technique, proves its worth in cardiology, neurology and cancer treatment
- Apple promotes the LaserWriter, a printer that will help to launch desktop publishing; the first desktop publishing and computer-aided design software is launched on the market later the same year
- Alec Jeffreys of the University of Leicester publishes his pioneering work on genetic fingerprinting in the journal *Nature*
- Kary Mullis of the USA unveils the polymerase chain reaction (PCR) technique, which enables biologists to multiply segments of DNA
- The Super Nintendo Entertainment System (SNES) console breathes new life into video games, originally introduced in 1958

▲ Desktop publishing

▲ Carl Sagan

◀ Pac-Man video game

1986

EVENTS

- Chernobyl nuclear disaster in the Ukraine (USSR)
- The space shuttle *Challenger* explodes minutes after take-off from Cape Canaveral
- Spain and Portugal join the European Community
- President Ferdinand Marcos flees the Philippines

INVENTIONS

- Canada's IMAX Corporation introduces IMAX 3-D
- Psion markets the Organiser II pocket computer, designed for use as a diary and notebook, helping to launch the era of personal digital assistants (PDAs)
- Charles W Hull patents the 3-D printing process known as stereolithography
- Researchers working with chimpanzees and bonobos provide fresh evidence of animal capacity for language
- DNA fingerprinting is used for the first time in a criminal investigation

1987

EVENTS

- By the Treaty of Washington, the USA and the USSR engage to remove intermediate-range nuclear missiles from Europe
- The First Intifada (uprising) breaks out against Israeli occupation of the Palestinian Territories
- Margaret Thatcher is elected for a third term in office

INVENTIONS

- The World Commission on Environment and Development, chaired by Gro Harlem Brundtland, produces a report that puts the concept of sustainable development on the international agenda
- US astronomers find evidence that stars are formed out of immense clouds of dust and gases
- New science parks and exploration centres attract crowds of visitors, drawn by innovative ways of presenting the fruits of science and technology in a hands-on format

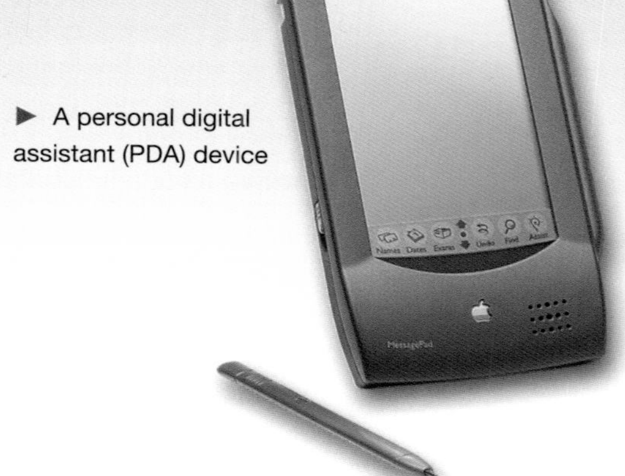

► A personal digital assistant (PDA) device

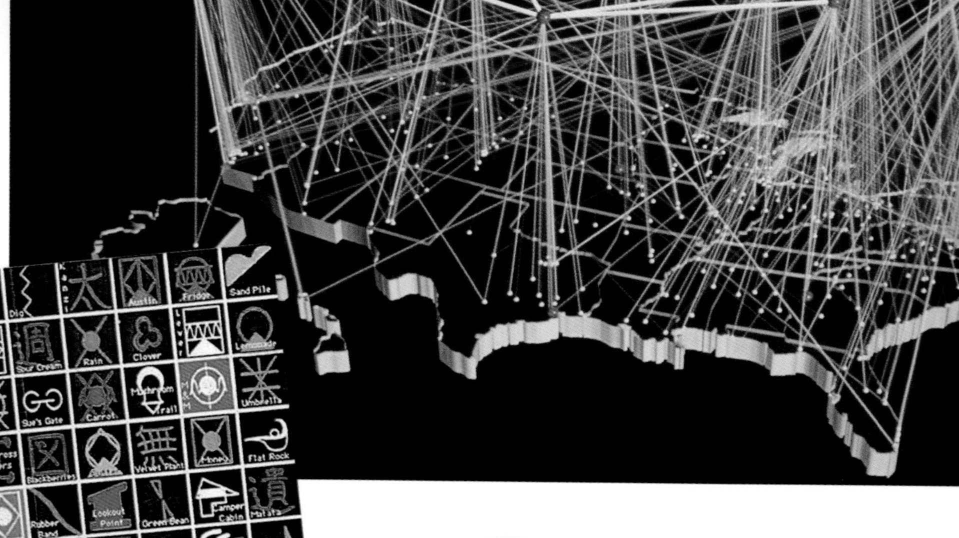

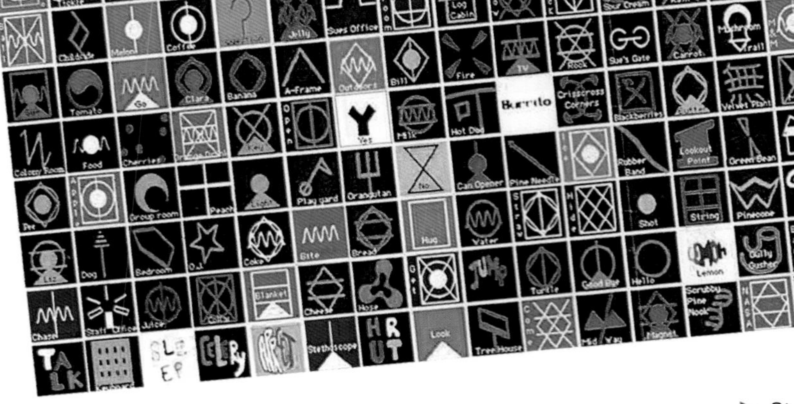

▼ Lexigrams learned by Kanzi, a bonobo, to communicate with human researchers

► Stereolithographic image of the inner ear of a fossil baboon

1988

- The Iran–Iraq War ends after eight years of fighting and the deaths of up to 1.5 million soldiers and thousands of civilians
- Benazir Bhutto becomes prime minister of Pakistan
- PanAm flight 103 explodes over Lockerbie
- NASA's James Hansen warns of global warming

- The Morris worm is one of the first computer viruses to be spread over the Internet
- Radio Data System (RDS) comes to the UK
- The 'morning after' abortion pill, developed by a French endocrinologist, is authorised for use in France
- The US government decides to finance the sequencing of the human genome
- Genetic engineering becomes the subject of fierce debate as critics point out possible abuses of the process, such as firms seeking to profit from the claim that individual genes can be linked to specific human qualities

1989

- Mikhail Gorbachev is named President of the USSR
- George Bush is sworn in as President of the USA
- Benazir Bhutto becomes prime minister of Pakistan
- Collapse of communism in eastern Europe; the Berlin Wall comes down
- China suppresses democracy protests in Tiananmen Square

- CERN, the European Organisation for Nuclear Research, improves its computer network by introducing hyperlinks, a key element of the budding Internet
- In Italy, Ferruzzi develops Mater-Bi®, a partially biodegradable plastic derived from corn starch
- Electronic tagging is introduced in England and Wales
- Marshall McLuhan's *The Global Village* is published posthumously, eight years after his death; the Canadian sociologist had established himself as a leading voice in the study of media and mass communications
- The first World Wide Web server is developed by Tim Berners-Lee

◄ Diagrammatic map of dataflow across the USA on the NSFNet

► LH95 star formation region

▼ Demonstrator protesting against excessive use of plastic packaging

1990

EVENTS

- Iraq invades Kuwait, starting the First Gulf War
- Akihito is crowned emperor of Japan
- Nelson Mandela is freed from prison in South Africa
- East and West Germany are reunited
- Thatcher resigns as PM and is succeeded by John Major

INVENTIONS

- Gene therapy gets underway in the USA where a team led by William Anderson and Michael Blaese, working for the National Institutes of Health, inject a patient with genetically modified versions of her own white blood cells
- The Hubble Space Telescope is placed in Earth orbit
- British and French workers tunnelling from both sides of the Channel greet each other deep under the seabed as the two ends of the Channel Tunnel link up; the tunnel will open for business in 1994

1991

EVENTS

- The break-up of Yugoslavia gets under way
- The USSR dissolves; most of the former Soviet republics proclaim independence; Boris Yeltsin is elected president of Russia
- UN coalition forces are victorious in the First Gulf War against Iraq
- Transpacific balloon flight by Per Lindstrand and Richard Branson

INVENTIONS

- The Japanese physicist Sumio Iijima discovers carbon nanotubes, opening the way to nanotechnology
- Kodak unveils its Digital Camera System (DCS), introducing digital photography to the mass market
- A large crater in Mexico is identified as the likely site of a massive prehistoric meteorite impact, supporting the theories of US father-and-son team Walter and Luis Alvarez on the extinction of the dinosaurs
- Car radio manufacturers adopt the EON (Enhanced Other Networks) system, an offshoot of RDS providing traffic information flashes that interrupt regular broadcasts and CDs

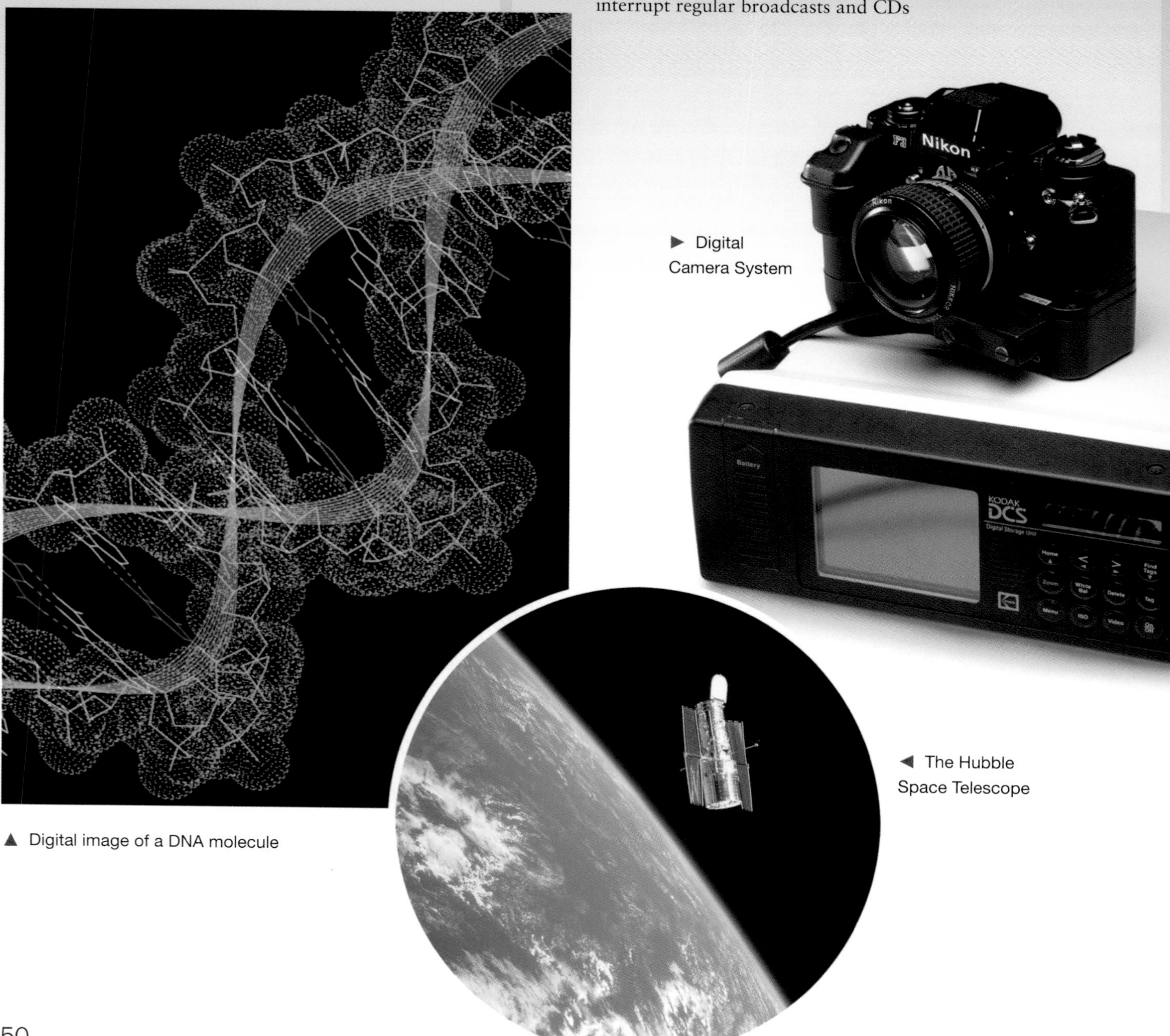

▶ Digital Camera System

▲ Digital image of a DNA molecule

◀ The Hubble Space Telescope

1992-3

- The Earth Summit is held under UN auspices in Rio de Janeiro (1992)
- Eritrea establishes independence from Ethiopia (1993)
- Vaclev Havel elected Czech president and parliament approves separation into two countries – Slovakia and the Czech Republic (1993)
- Bill Clinton sworn in as 42nd President of the USA (1993)

- James Dyson launches the bagless vacuum cleaner
- Shuji Nakamura of Japan produces the first high-brightness blue-light LEDs
- The digital imagery in Steven Spielberg's *Jurassic Park* impresses a worldwide cinema-going audience
- CERN puts software initially created by Tim Berners-Lee in the public domain, helping to launch the World Wide Web
- The first webcam goes into service on the Internet

1994

- Genocide in Rwanda
- Nelson Mandela is elected president of the Republic of South Africa in the first elections involving all South Africans
- Kim Jong-il succeeds Kim Il-Sung as the ruler of North Korea
- The IRA declares a ceasefire in northern Ireland

- US mathematician Peter Shor demonstrates that it might be possible to develop quantum computers
- In the course of the 1990s high-performance materials, which have already revolutionised the world of sports, successfully move into mass market products
- Apple markets QuickTake, the first digital colour camera

▼ Eric Tabarly on board the *Paul Ricard* during his record-breaking Atlantic voyage

▼ A magnet levitating at very low temperature above a superconductor

▼ Digital imagery in a scene from *Jurassic Park*

1995

EVENTS

- The World Trade Organisation is founded
- Israel's prime minister Yitzhak Rabin is assassinated by a right-wing Israeli extremist
- US shuttle docks with Russian space station Mir

INVENTIONS

- DVDs are launched by a consortium of companies comprising Philips, Sony, Hitachi, JVC, Matsushita, Mitsubishi, Pioneer, Thomson, Time Warner and Toshiba
- The Proton prepaid cash card is introduced in Belgium, building on a stored-value card system previously tested in Denmark

A counterfeit banknote detection system, the Incontournable ('Indispensable'), is developed by Stéphane Dufils in France

- Two Swiss astronomers, Michel Mayor and Didier Quéloz, are the first to announce the discovery of an exoplanet (a planet orbiting a distant star)
- Using information transmitted by satellite, the Global Positioning System (GPS) enables users to establish their exact location

1996

EVENTS

- The First Chechen War comes to an end
- France ends its nuclear testing in the Pacific
- Israel launches a 16-day blitz on Lebanon
- The Taliban seize Kabul, the Afghan capital
- Benjamin Netanyahu elected Israeli prime minister

INVENTIONS

- Dolly the sheep is born, the first mammal to be cloned from an adult cell
- E-commerce becomes established on the Internet
- Microsoft launches NetMeeting, enabling users to access telephone services over the Internet
- High-definition digital programming is first broadcast by television channels in the USA
- The Israeli company Mirabilis introduces ICQ, an instant-messaging computer program

▲ The annual ferry race held in Sydney Harbour

► Counterfeit note detector

▼ Blue laser

1997

- The Taliban extend their power over much of Afghanistan
- Russia joins the G7 group of industrialised nations, turning it into the G8
- Tony Blair becomes British Prime Minister
- Hong Kong returns to Chinese rule

- The first plasma TV screens go on sale
- Toyota launches the Prius, the first mass-market hybrid car combining gasoline and electric propulsions systems
- An MP3 player is displayed at the CeBIT computer exhibition in Hanover, Germany
- Originating in Japan in 1984, the concept of functional (or medicinal) food – food enriched with vitamins and minerals to promote health and combat diseases as well as to provide nutrition – goes global

1998

- Pol Pot dies in Cambodia
- In Northern Ireland voters back the Good Friday peace accord in a referendum
- Most countries in the EU agree to introduce a single European currency

- ADSL – the Asymmetric Digital Subscriber Line – makes it possible to send data down telephone lines
- Teams of astronomers at the University of California in Berkeley find evidence that the expansion of the universe is accelerating
- Pfizer develops and markets Viagra as a treatment for erectile dysfunction
- IBM develops a two-qubit quantum computer

1999

- The Scottish Parliament is opened
- Mohammed VI becomes king of Morocco
- Abdullah II ascends the throne of Jordan on the death of his father King Hussein
- The Kosovo War ends
- Thabo Mbeki succeeds Nelson Mandela

- WiFi and Bluetooth bring wireless transmission technologies to the Internet
- Trik Technology and IBM develop USB flash drives
- Digital notebooks that can download handwriting appear on the market
- Larry Sanger and Jimmy Wales create Wikipedia, a Web-based encyclopaedia free to all users

▼ Electronic cash

▼ 51 Pegasus b, an exoplanet of the star 51 Pegasus

Index

Page numbers in *italics* refer to captions.

Picture credits

ABBREVIATIONS: t = top, c = centre, b = bottom, l = left, r = right

Front cover: main image, a scientist examining a DNA autoradiogram, TEK Image/Science Photo Library. **Inset:** Game Boy console, Corbis/H Le Tourneur. **Spine**: light-emitting diode, Cosmos/SPL/ M F Chillmaid.
Back cover: 'Manny', a US military test dummy, Cosmos/SPL/US Dept of Energy.
Page 2, left to right, top row: CERN/Cosmos/SPL/Laguna Design; Corbis/H Le Tourneur; REA/LAIF/S Elleringmann; 2nd row: REA/ROPI/Fotogramma/Cattaneo; NASA/STS; Cosmos/SPL/P Wooton; 3rd row: Cosmos/SPL/Pasieka; Cosmos/SPL/S Sambraus/T Luddington; REA/A Derouard; bottom row: Cosmos/SSPL; Corbis/S Huffaker; Cosmos/SPL/J Greig.
Pages 4/5: Arecibo radio telescope in Puerto Rico, David Parker/Science Photo Library.
6t: © 2003 Nintendo; 6l: Cosmos/SPL/D Parker; 6/7: NASA; 7t: Corbis/S Huffaker; 7d: Cosmos/SPL/Dr T Evans; 7c: NASA/Ames Research Center; 8t: Cosmos/SPL/V De Schlamberg; 8/9: Cosmos/ SPL/J King-Holmes; 8b: Cosmos/SPL/B Svensson; 9tr: REA/A Devouard; 9bl: BSIP/Photo Researchers; 9br: Corbis/Ausloeser; 10l: NASA/MSFC; 10/11: Getty Images/Bloomberg; 10br: Inserm/M Depardieu; 11tr: Corbis/Science Faction/L Psihoyos; 11br: REA/H Berti, Kinémax (Futuroscope, Poitiers), architect: Denis Laming; 12/13t: Corbis/C Lovell; 12bl: Cosmos/SPL/Animate4.com; 12br: Musée français de la Photographie, Briéves; 13tl: Cosmos/SPL/M F Chillmaid; 13bl: Corbis/San Francisco Chronicle/M Macor; 13br: Cosmos/SPL/C Dominguez; 14t: CERN/Maximilien Brice; 14bl: Getty Images/Allsport/Michael Cooper; 14/15b: Cosmos/SPL/S Sambraus/T Luddington; 15l: Roger Viollet/Philippe Joffre/Nam June Paik, 1989, Paris, Museum of Modern Art; 15r: Cosmos/SPL/W Steger; 16tr: Cosmos/ESO; 16l: Phanie/SPL/J King-Holmes; 16br: NASA; 17l: Cosmos/SPL/US Dept of Energy; 17r: Corbis/E Kashi; 19tc: Getty Images/SSPL; 18/19: REA/LAIF/S Elleringmann; 20t: Cosmos/SPL/D Parker; 20c: Getty Images/SSPL; 20bl: AFP/O Torres; 21tr: AFP/N Millauer; 21bl: Corbis/Xinhua Press/Zhang Ning; 22t: Cosmos/SPL/Dr T Evans; 22b: Cosmos/SPL/NIBSC/R Longuehaye; 23tr: Vivat Direct Ltd; 23b: APF/D Perrault; 24t: © 2003 Nintendo; 24bl: Corbis/Classic Stock/J C Towers; 25b: Cosmos/SSPL; 25tl: Getty Images/SSPL; 25r: Corbis/H Le Tourneur; 26t: AFP/G Bouys; 26c: Cosmos/SPL/J Greig; 26b: Corbis/Sygma/J Heklmian; 27t: AFP/WWF; 27b: Getty Images/Hulton Archives/Apic; 28bl: Corbis/Science Faction/L Psihoyos; 28/29b: TCD Prod DB/DR, *Jurassic Park III*, 2001, Amblin/Universal; 29t: Corbis/Cat's Collection; 29b: NASA/Ames Research Center; 30tl: AFP/Arte Factory/M Mimram; 30c: Corbis/EPA/Yonhap; 30bl: NASA/Ames Research Center; 31t: REA/D Maillac; 31b: Computer History Museum/University of Utah; 32tl: AFP/Th A Clary; 32br: Getty Images/Wireimage/A L Ortega; 33tl: Cosmos/SSPL; 33tr: The Kobal Collection, *Avatar*, 2009, Twentieth Century-Fox Film Corporation; 33b: Corbis/S Huffaker; 34t: Cosmos/SSPL; 34b: Corbis/K Tiegde; 35t: Corbis/Sygma/A Serra; 35c: Didier Descouens; 35b: KevS; 36t: Corbis/E Kreutz; 36b: AFP/A Scorza; 37t: Corbis/Sygma/J Guichard; 37br: Cosmos/SPL/Bluestone; 38l: NASA; 38c: ESO; 39t & 39c: NASA; 40t: Great Ape Trust; 40b: Corbis/R Friedman; 41t: Cosmos/SPL/S Kuklin; 42cr: Corbis/Itar Tass/Y Mashlov; 42bl: Corbis/Sygma/J L Atlan; 43t: Corbis/G Smith; 43br: AFP/Kort Duce; 44/45t: REA/LAIF/S Elleringmann; 44c: REA/A Derouard; 44bl: Cosmos/SPL/Bluestone; 46/47t: Cosmos/SPL/Phantatomix; 46c: Cosmos/SPL/M Krzywinski; 46b: Cosmos/SPL/J King-Holmes; 47br: Institut Pasteur, Paris; 48t: Corbis/Bettemann; 48b: Cosmos/Aurora/T Bigelow; 49t: Fedefoto/J M Marin; 49b: Cosmos/SPL/S Ogden; 50tr: Corbis/A Brusso; 50cl: CERN; 51tl: Collection Ed Thelen; 51br: Cosmos/SPL/NCSA/University of Illinois; 52tl: Getty Images/Iconica/Jetta Productions; 52tc: Cosmos/SPL/Laguna Design; 52/53: Getty Images/C Mitchelldyer; 53br: Cosmos/SPL/Caida; 54t: Cosmos/SPL/J Mason; 54l: REA/R Desmaret; 55t: The Kobal Collection, *You've Got Mail*, 1998, Warner Bros; 55b: Cosmos/SPL/B Svensson; 56tl: Cosmos/SPL/Ch Darkin; 56/57t: Computer History Museum/Gift of Google; 56/57c: Cosmos/SPL/V De Schlamberg; 56c: Corbis/T Bird; 56b: Corbis/EPA/K J Hildenbrand; 57cd: Getty Images/Photographer's Choice/A Reynolds; 57c: Corbis/Monsoon Photolibrary/R Cattan; 57br: Cosmos/SPL/M Sykes; 58tl: Getty Images © 2006 Phil Schermeister; 58cr: REA/ROPI/Fotogramma/Cattaneo; 58bl: REA/Ludovic; 59t: Corbis/Ausloeser; 59b: Corbis/C A Gonzalez; 60l: Cosmos/SPL/W & D McIntyre; 60br: Cosmos/SPL/Pr. S Cohen; 61t: Corbis/O Martel; 61b: Cosmos/SPL/Laguna Design; 62t: Look at Sciences/P Plailly; 62l: REA/P Allard; 63t: Corbis/G Steimetz; 63b: BSIP/Photo Researchers; 64tl: REA/A Devouard; 64/65: Inserm/P Latron; 65bl: REA/P Allard; 65br: Inserm/T Touboul; 66/67: AFP/Pavani; 66b: Inserm/M Depardieu; 67r: Prod DB/DR, *Splice*, 2009, Gaumont; 67b: Corbis/M Kulka; 68/69, 69t & 69b: NASA/MSFC; 70: NASA/Kennedy Space Center; 70cl: NASA/STS; 71t: NASA/Hubble Space Collection; 71b (2): NASA/Great Images in NASA Collection; 72 & 73t: NASA; 73b: NASA/MSFC; 74t: Corbis/J Zukermann; 74bl: Cosmos/SPL/D Van Ravenswaay; 75tr: Corbis/Science Faction/C Brinkema; 75b: Corbis/Science Faction/L Psihoyos; 76c: REA/B Decout; 77t: Getty Images/SSPL; 77cr: Getty Images/Dorling Kindersley/A Crawford; 77bl: Getty Images/Bloomberg; 78t: REA/H Berti, Kinémax (Futuroscope, Poitiers), architect: Denis Laming; 78b: Corbis/Arcaid/J Helle, Musée Nemo, Amsterdam, architect: Renzo Piano; 79bl: Corbis/L V Bergman; 79r: AFP/Pavani; 80t: Corbis/C & A Purcell; 80b: Corbis/R Finn Hestoft; 81t: Getty Images/Time&Life/T Thaï; 81b: AFP/P Andrieu; 82t: AFP/A Jocard; 82b: REA/*The New York Times*/E S Lesser; 83: Corbis/G Steinmetz; 84tl: Getty Images/Aurora/C Wolinsky; 84c: Cosmos/SPL/Pasieka; 85t: Cosmos/SPL/Dr P Harris; 85bl: IBM; 85br: Getty Images/ScienceFoto/H U Danzebrick; 86t: Cosmos/SPL/Animate4.com; 86b: Getty Images/ScienceFoto/U Bellhsuser; 87: Cosmos/SPL/Dr A Yazdani & Dr D J Hornbaker; 88t: Cosmos/SPL/USA Air Force; 88b: Saint-Gobain Glass France; 89t Getty Images/ScienceFoto/U Bellhsuser; 89b: Cosmos/SPL/NBNL; 90/91t: Corbis/Xinhua Press/Zhang Jiayu; 90cl: Corbis/San Francisco Chronicle/M Macor; 90b: Corbis/R Ressmeyer; 91br: REA/LAIF/G Knechtel; 92t: Corbis/G Steimetz; 92b: Cosmos/SPL/T Craddock; 93bl: Cosmos/SPL/M Stock; 93br: Cosmos/SPL/C Dominguez; 94t: Corbis/M Cristofori; 94b: Corbis/A Wright; 95tr: AFP/H P Van Velthoven; 95bl: Cosmos/SPL/S Terry; 96tr: Cosmos/SSPL/NMeM; 96c: Cosmos/SPL/V De Schlamberg; 96/97b, 97br: Corbis/Science Faction/D Scharf; 98tl: Musée français de la Photographie, Biévres; 98b: Cosmos/SPL/P Wooton; 99t: Corbis/Sygma/R Siemonet, *Matrix*, 1999; 99b: Corbis/DPA/W Langenstrassen; 100t: Corbis/C Lovell; 100b: Corbis/T Latham; 101t: SIPA/AP/J Scott Applewhite; 101b: Corbis/S Frink; 102t: REA/N Tavernier; 102c: Corbis/EPA/M Gambarini; 102b: Cosmos/SPL/M F Chillmaid; 103t: Getty Images/Allsport/Michael Cooper; 103b: Corbis/Schlegmilch; 104tl: Cosmos/SPL/IMI/University of Birmingham HT Consortium/D Parker; 104b: Cosmos/SPL/Los Alamos National Laboratory; 104/105: Corbis/Sygma/J Guichard; 105b: Cosmos/SPL/Chemical Design Ltd; 106tl: The Kobal Collection/MGM/*Dr Jekyll & Mr Hyde*, 1941; 106cr: © Éditions Blake et Mortimer/Studio Jacobs n.v. (Dargaud-Limbard s.a.); 107t: The Kobal Collection/CCC, *Flesh for Frankenstein*, 1973; 107b: The Kobal Collection/Nero, *Dr Mabuse*, 1933; 108t: The Kobal Collection/Amblin/Universal, *Back to the Future*, 1985; 108b: Prod DB/Hawks Film/DR, *Dr Strangelove*, 1964; 109: The Kobal Collection/Ufa, *Metropolis*, 1926; 109: Corbis/ Bettemann, *The Hound of Baskervilles*, 1939; 110t: The Kobal Collection/Marvel/20th Century Fox, *X-Men Origins: Wolverine*, 2009; 110/111b: The Kobal Collection/20th Century Fox, *The Day After Tomorrow*, 2004; 110bl: Prod DB/Danjac-Eon/DR, *Dr No*, 1962; 111tr: The Kobal Collection/Ladd Company/Warner Bros, *Blade Runner*, 1982; 112: Cosmos/SPL/M Kulyk; 113br: National Institute of Standards and Technology/J Jost; 113t: Cosmos/SPL/W Steger; 115tr: RMN/CNAC/MNAM Dist. RMN/ J Hyde/*Unendliche Schleife* ('*Ribbon without End*'), version IV, Bill Max ADAGP, Paris 2010; 115lcl & bc: Pascal Goetgheluck; 116tr: Roger Viollet/Philippe Joffre/Musée d'Art Moderne, Nam June Paik 1989, Paris, Musée d'Art Moderne; 116bl: RMN/Collection Centre Pompidou, Dist. RMN/Philippe Migeat/Bruce Nauman ADAGP, Paris 2010; 117: Getty Images/Time Life Pictures/ S Berger; 118/119: AFP/R Rivas/*The Crossing*, Bill Viola, The Guggenheim Bilbao Museum, June 2004-Jan 2005; 118l: Corbis/S Touhig; 118b: Arno Ginsinger/Esther Shalev-Gerz, Musée du Jeu de Paume, Feb-June 2010, Paris ADAGP, Paris 2010; 119b: Corbis/M Bryan Makela; 120t: Cosmos/SPL/S Sambraus/T Luddington; 120b: Cosmos/SPL/Eye of Science; 121t: BSIP/GIPhoto Stock/Photo Researchers, Inc; 121r: *Terminator 2* Blu-ray cover, Ronald Grant Archive/Mary Evans; 122: Corbis/ R Talaie; 123t: Corbis/G Steimetz; 123r: Cosmos/ SPL/Ria Novosti; 123c: Cosmos/SPL/S Terry; 123b: Cosmos/SPL/J Coney; 124t: Phanie/SPL/ J King-Holmes; 124l: Cosmos/SPL/M Mayo/King-Holmes; 125t: Cosmos/SPL/J King-Holmes; 125c: REA/S Ortola; 125b: Cosmos/SPL/Pasieka; 126/127: AFP/A De Groot; 126l: AFP/Handout; 127r: Getty Images/SSPL/NRM/Pictorial Collection; 127b: REA/R Damoret; 128tr: Look at Sciences/ M Brega; 128bl: REA/S Audras; 129c: Pascal Goetgheluck; 129br: REA/LAIF/A Teichmann; 130t: Reuters/T Melville; 130br: Cosmos/SPL/US Dept of Energy; 131tl: REA/LAIF/Rl. Bermes; 131tr: The Kobal Collection/Carolco, *Terminator II*, 1991; 131b: REA/R Unkel; 132t: REA/Redux/T Law; 132cl: REA/Expansion/J Chatain; 133b: REA/Reporters/M Gronemberger; 134t: Corbis/Sygma/J P Laffont; 134/135: Cosmos/SPL; 134cr: NASA; 134b: NASA/Solarsystem Collection; 136: Cosmos/SPL/D Darby; 137cd: NASA/ESA/C Carreau; 137bd: NASA/JPL-Caltech/ESA/Institut d'astrophysique de Paris; 138t: ESA/CNES/D Ducros; 138b: ESO/L Calcada; 139t: NASA/Karen Wehrstein (http://www.artofkaren.blogspot.com); 139b: Cosmos/ESO; 140l: Corbis/E Kashi; 140br: Hemis.fr/F Guiziou; 141t: Leemage/Imagestate/S Thomson; 141l: AGE Fotostock/R Matina; 142t: REA/Panos/R Wallis; 142/143: Corbis/F Soltan; 142bl: Getty Images/A Murrell; 143b: REA/Panos/J Horner; 144/145: Corbis/S Huffaker; 146l: Corbis/Cat's Collection; 146r: AFP/O Torres; 147l: NASA Solarsystem Collection; 147r: Vivat Direct; 147b: Corbis/ClassicStock/J C Towers; 148tl: Cosmos/SSPL; 148bl: Great Ape Trust; 148/149: Cosmos/SPL/NCSA/University of Illinois; 148br: Didier Descouens; 149tr: NASA; 149b: Corbis/C A Gonzalez; 150l: Cosmos/SPL/W & D McIntyre; 150tr: Cosmos/SSPL/NMeM; 150b: NASA/MSFC; 151tl: Cosmos/SPL/IMI/University of Birmingham HT Consortium/D Parker; 151b: TCD Prod DB/DR, *Jurassic Park III*, 2001, Amblin/Universal; 151r: Corbis/Sygma/J Guichard; 152tl: AFP/A De Groot; 152tr: REA/Expansion/J Chatain; 154b: BSIP/GIPhotoStock/Photo Researchers, Inc; 155l: REA/Reporters/M Gronemberger; 155r: Cosmos/SPL/D Darby.

Illustrations on pages 116 (bits and qubits) and 137t (hunting exoplanets) by Grégoire Cirade.

THE ADVENTURE OF DISCOVERIES AND INVENTIONS
Genetic Innovation – 1985 to 1995
Published in 2011 in the United Kingdom by Vivat Direct Limited
(t/a Reader's Digest), 157 Edgware Road, London W2 2HR

Adapted from *L'Ère du Génie Génétique*, part of a series entitled L'ÉPOPÉE DES DÉCOUVERTES ET DES INVENTIONS, created in France by BOOKMAKER and first published by Sélection du Reader's Digest, Paris, in 2011.

Translated from French by Tony Allan

PROJECT TEAM
Series editor Christine Noble
Art editor Julie Bennett
Designers Martin Bennett, Simon Webb
Consultant Ruth Binney
Proofreader Ron Pankhurst
Indexer Marie Lorimer

Colour origination FMG
Printed and bound in China

VIVAT DIRECT
Editorial director Julian Browne
Art director Anne-Marie Bulat
Managing editor Nina Hathway
Picture resource manager Sarah Stewart-Richardson
Technical account manager Dean Russell
Product production manager Claudette Bramble
Production controller Sandra Fuller

We are committed both to the quality of our products and the service we provide to our customers. We value your comments, so please feel free to contact us on 0871 351 1000 or via our website at **www.readersdigest.co.uk**

If you have any comments or suggestions about the content of our books, you can email us at **gbeditorial@readersdigest.co.uk**

CONCEPT CODE: FR0104/IC/S
BOOK CODE: 642-014 UP0000-1
ISBN: 978-0-276-44526-2